QUARTET ENCOUNTERS

PAINTINGS

Segalen wrote *Paintings* between 1911–16. Completely and daringly informed by Chinese metaphysics both in subject matter and structure, the text is an amalgam of controlled hallucinations, 'spoken paintings'. These word-images, though placed in an 'historical' context, throw into relief Segalen's preoccupation with the contradictions between the real and the imagined. He invents not only a new way of seeing, but a new vision of words. As Mallarmé said: 'Writing is present in the margins, painting is spread over "vacant" space.' Here, vision is double, words are doubled; we are invited to pass beyond the mirror. Segalen proposes his raking vision of the relationship between words and sounds, images and fictive things, between desire and its object. A metaphysical journey of great intensity and complexity, of quicksilver-playfulness, of mystic nihilism and luminary magic, *Paintings* is an extraordinary and unclassifiable work by a philosophic poet of genius and a supreme innovator.

VICTOR SEGALEN

Victor Segalen, doctor, traveller, librettist, philosopher, poet, novelist, archaeologist and sinologist, was born in Brest in 1878. He first visited China in 1908 and there organized an archaeological expedition in search of monuments of the Han Dynasty. Later, his brilliant study of Chinese sculpture was acclaimed a masterpiece by André Malraux. His friendship with Claudel, Perse, Jouve and Debussy was to influence their work as well as his own. He died in mysterious circumstances in the forest of Heulgoat, Brittany, in 1919. Segalen left behind him works of astonishing diversity.

René Leys is also available in the Quartet Encounters series.

VICTOR SEGALEN

Paintings

Translated from the French and with an
Introduction by ANDREW HARVEY and IAIN WATSON

Quartet Books

For
Gini Alhadeff

First published in Great Britain by
Quartet Books Limited 1991
A member of the Namara Group
27/29 Goodge Street
London W1P 1FD

Originally published in French under the title *Peintures* in 1916

British Library Cataloguing in Publication Data
Segalen, Victor
Paintings
I. Title II. [Peintures]. *English*
843.912 [F]

ISBN 0 7043 0152 0

Typeset by Contour Typesetters, Southall, London
Printed and bound by
BPCC Hazell Books, Aylesbury, Bucks, England
Member of BPCC Ltd

CONTENTS

INTRODUCTION

That Segalen is amongst the most sophisticated, astute, and disturbing of modern visionaries is one of the best kept secrets of twentieth-century literature. Just before he died, Borges remarked to a French poet friend of ours: 'The French talk about Valéry and even the preposterous Peguy with adoration – don't they know that in Victor Segalen they have one of the most intelligent writers of our age, perhaps the only one to have made a fresh synthesis of Western and Eastern aesthetics and philosophy?' Our French friend had not heard of Segalen and said so. Borges hid his face in his hands and groaned. 'My dear L,' he murmured, 'do not live another month before you have read the entire *oeuvre*.' Then he started to laugh: 'You can read Segalen in less than a month, but it might take you the rest of your life to begin to understand him.'

Victor Segalen was born in Brest in 1878 and died in 1919, in a wood near Heulgoat in Brittany, of a mysterious wasting illness, with *Hamlet* open by his side. In the course of his relatively short life, he was a doctor, traveller, librettist, philosopher, poet, novelist and archaeologist. He left behind him a work of astonishing diversity; his books include *Les Immémoriaux* (which remains the subtlest book ever written by a Westerner about Polynesia), written at the age of twenty-four after a visit to the Marquesas, *Siddharta*, a libretto on the life of the Buddha which he wrote for Debussy, brilliant short studies on Rimbaud and Gauguin, and a cluster of masterpieces inspired by his long stay in China from 1906 to 1916: *Stèles, Equipée, René Leys, Le Fils du Ciel* and *Peintures*. The scorched and fading photos that survive of Segalen show a haughty, lean, handsome face with the eyes of a mystic apache, of a man of intricate disdains, drastic ironies and just as drastic a capacity for reverence. To take Borges's suggestion and read Segalen's entire *oeuvre* is to undertake a metaphysical journey of great intensity and complexity. Segalen writes towards the end of *Peintures*: 'Only the painter and those who know how to see have access to magical space.' This 'access to magical space' was Segalen's reward for his passion and long solitude, and his fierce gift to those willing to travel with him.

The blessing of Segalen's life, and the inspiration of his best and most exacting work, was his discovery of China, of a world as elaborate, hieratic, terrifying and mysterious as his own deepest imagination. Late Manchu China in its chaos and sumptuousness, its mystical cult of the 'hidden' Emperor, in the profusion and radiance of its still-existent schools of Buddhism and Taoism was for Segalen the 'place and the formula', the long-desired encounter with a landscape and history and spiritual tradition that fulfilled his wildest and most exalted fantasies. From the beginning of his stay in China, Segalen understood that the secret meaning of his life and the secret of China were intextricably intertwined. As he wrote to a friend: 'In the end it was not a creation of China itself that I came to look for but a vision of China ... and I hold on to that with my teeth.' China awoke Segalen's own visionary imagination because it constantly confronted him with the impenetrable both in the world and in himself: out of the excited but intellectually fastidious and precise meeting between his Western intellect honed on Nietzsche and the Buddhist and Taoist philosophies of China came the great work of his late period, a work that is neither 'Western' nor 'Eastern', but a strange and haunting hybrid of both, a work in which the assumptions of Eastern and Western aesthetics and philosophy are flung against each other with expert savagery and re-combined in startling ways. As Segalen wrote in fragments of an essay on 'Exoticism' (an essay that was to sum up his vision of life but which was never completed): 'Exoticism is not that kaleidoscopic state of the tourist and of the mediocre spectator... but the live and curious reaction to the *shock of a strong* individual against an objectivity it perceives and whose distance it savours.' He adds later: 'Exoticism ... is not an adaptation ... not the comprehension of a beyond-itself that one could then embrace into oneself... but the *sharp and direct perception of something eternally incomprehensible*' (our italics). To keep 'sharp' and 'direct' perception that is trained – relentlessly – on the incomprehensible demands the rarest and finest kind of intellect – one that is at once capable of protean reverence (each of Segalen's 'Chinese' works is a different experiment in Homage) and of an unwavering fidelity to solitude and detachment. Segalen said of himself, conscious, of course, of all the levels of paradox that he was playing with, that he was a 'proud mystic', ferociously unattached to any kind of religious dogma, but 'in awe of the indefinable' of that 'China-behind and beyond-the-world' he refers to in one of his last letters. To keep alive this proud mystical self, to allow himself to be crucified on its continuing and continually fertile contradictions without allowing himself any of the ways out of its exposure that he might have taken – into less faith, less cynicism, or silence – was Segalen's courage as a human being; from that courage were born the powers of analytic ecstasy and sardonic exultation that inform and illumine his work.

Peintures, finished in 1916 after six years' labour, is in some ways the strangest of the 'Chinese' works, and the one most completely and daringly informed by Chinese metaphysics, both in its subject matter and its aesthetic structure. Although Segalen had withering things to say about Buddhism's life-weariness and contempt for the body and never in any 'official' way became a Taoist, he had enormous (and very well-informed) curiosity about the higher metaphysics of both religions and felt temperamentally akin to Lao Tzu. The lightness of tone of *Peintures* and its wild playfulness of structure derive their depth and their intensity from Segalen's immersion in the Taoist and Buddhist vision of the universe. In Buddhism, as the *Prajnaparamita Sutra* puts it, 'Emptiness is form; form emptiness'; what the senses perceive – wrongly – as solid is in fact incessantly projected from a Void, whose essential luminous emptiness is the true nature of all phenomena. In Taoism this universe – what Lao Tzu calls the 'ten thousand things' – has its source in the Tao, the governing power of the cosmos, and is in continual movement within and against the Tao's rapt, immobile but infinitely creative calm. Reality is a phantasmagoria, a rush of electric, transforming, transient energies that spring out of and flow back into a blissful vacancy. Both Buddhism and Taoism, then, view reality not as, in the Western sense, an architectural structure but as a collection of phenomena perpetually oscillating between appearance and disappearance. For both philosophies, moreover, the 'spectator' of the 'play' is as unreal, finally, as the 'play' itself. As Şantideva says in the *Bodhicharyavatara*: 'If that which is seen is as unreal as illusion, then so is the one who sees the mind.' An unreal person is watching an unreal 'parade' (to use Segalen's own description of *Peintures*) in which every possible combination of possibilities can – and will – occur but in which nothing, in the final analysis, exists. Liberation for Taoist and Buddhist consists in the unwavering awareness of this essential unreality, and in the magical power, humour and love that is released from this awareness and devastation of all possible clinging to appearances or to any of the vanities of a fictitious self.

It is this vision – of the fantastical flux of the cosmos and of the essential non-existence of both 'parade' and spectator – that *Peintures* is dedicated to 'embodying' (the word in such a context has a more than ironic ring). Segalen's hills in *Peintures* are mobile, his fans are agitated by their own energy, the lacquers swim suddenly under the glare of hidden lights, the vicious Empresses and their consorts reveal themselves as pioneers of bizarre virtue. The reader himself is exhorted, bullied, teased in frequently contradictory ways that compel him to give up the safety of considered judgement and force him into plunging – with the writer-creator's own abandon – into the hilarious and terrible dance of the world. *Peintures* has the same lack of structure, the same endless ambiguity, the same incessantly dissolving nature as Reality itself – viewed through illumined Buddhist or Taoist eyes. In Segalen's work as in Lao Tzu's or Şantideva's, no irony is without its secret transcendent opposite, no transcendence without its shadow of derision or derangement, no vice without its inherent possibility of virtue, no object exists that cannot, under certain special conditions, melt into another, equally deceptive shape, no rhetoric of presentation can be paraded that does not disguise as much as it discloses, that does not disguise in fact by pretending to disclose. All is flux and fantasy, all is theatrical in the highest, wildest, saddest and most liberating sense of the word. If there is any truth it is in the cold hard blue autumn sky, perpetually unstained by such shenannigans as 'human history', which saves (if it can be said to 'save') by being blankly detached.

In *Peintures* all the standard securities of Western writing are dissolved, all nineteenth-century beliefs in Virtue, Progress and the amiable and tractable solidity of reality are implicitly and explicitly derided, all traditional Western distinctions between 'reader', 'writer', 'language' and 'world' are collapsed vehemently into each other in an extraordinary and insolent act of metaphysical prestidigitatation whose ingenuity is at once liberating and menacing, brilliant and vacant with the brilliance and vacancy of Illusion itself spun endlessly, without any 'interpretable' meaning, out of the Void. *Peintures* is a mystic cabaret by a polymorphous perverse philosophic poet of genius. Nothing is safe from the irreverence of Segalen's mind – not even some of the most cherished beliefs of Chinese civilization itself – as in the parade of exuberant monsters in *Peintures Dynastiques* that savages all Confucian and conventional Buddhist notions of 'Virtue'. But as with Lao Tzu and the highest *mahayana* metaphysics, such relentless irreverence is itself a form of reverence, a merciless honouring of a Truth that lies beyond dogma, beyond formulation, beyond all kinds of language, beyond society in a limitless freedom that is the secret identity and only real glory of consciousness itself. The Buddha refused to define the Truth in anything but the most negative terms, so as to preserve its perpetual virgin astonishment; behind the parade of *Peintures* there is a similar belief in a Truth too high and too mysterious to be defiled by language, a Truth which is barely even alluded to but which, as the work is read again and again, comes to be the one true, constant Actor.

Translating such a work of resourceful mystic nihilism is an exhausting task. Style and meaning in *Peintures* are one and the same thing and Segalen's style can veer, in one paragraph, from grandiose vision to irony to frivolity and all the way round and back again through the various ornate and frivolous registers of French. To remain faithful to Segalen's 'magical surface' and the philosophical intentions behind its shifting movements required endless revisions. What began as an act of love became something like a metaphysical journey into the heart of the English language – a language that had in some subtle ways to be re-made to mirror Segalen's lapidary ferocities and quicksilver deracinations. We chose to preserve at all costs the strangeness of the original, and tried never to betray its electric perversities for simpler satisfactions. Nothing in our 're-creation' of *Peintures* has been smoothed out; no falsely 'helpful' connections have been made; all abruptness of syntax and alarming jumps of thought and address have been preserved as far as possible. We have tried an English happily deranged at moments to mirror the derangement of the original to recreate an antic visionary prose-poem that compromises neither with 'reality' nor the 'reader'.

Our inspiration throughout – sometimes badly needed – has been the hidden and mischievous centre of *Peintures* – the figure of the Master Painter, who is always blind-drunk and who finds 'the link of light uniting for ever joy and life'. It is this link of light that for the Buddhist and Taoist runs under the entire play of life, that connects and binds together all Segalen's shifts and poses, and this link and its light we hope sparkles underneath and in our English version. *Peintures* is, as Segalen wrote, an *'oeuvre réciproque'*, demanding of the reader (and translators) something of the writer's own power of abandon and 'drunken clairvoyance'; over several years we tried to rise to Segalen's cruel and marvellous challenge. 'One is one. Two even is one if you so desire it. Nothing of what you touch daily has solidity . . . only the painter and those who know how to see have access to magical space.'

Andrew Harvey and Iain Watson

Paintings

Ces Peintures, littéraires,
sont offertes en retour des siennes
magnifiquement picturales,
au Maître-Peintre et grand Ami

GEORGE DANIEL DE MONFREID

You are there: you wait, decided perhaps to listen to me right until the end; but destined or no to see clearly, without modesty, to see all right up until the end? – I do not in any way exact promises: I do not wish for any other reply or help but those of silence and your eyes. First, have you any idea of what is shown here and why this PARADE takes place? These are Chinese paintings; long, dark silken paintings, stiff with soot and coloured by primeval time. Some should be unrolled from top to bottom; I shall have them suspended, each in turn, from the height of *this* rafter down to the ground. Those which cannot be moved or bought (mere gilded rubbings at the ends of caves, reflections in the depth of lacquer or of eyes), I shall notwithstanding deliver up to you: they are Magical Paintings. One other, unique, shall be unrolled horizontally between the two hands which hold it: it is the defilade of the Cortèges and the Trophy of the Tributes of Kingdoms. However, you must by yourselves reach, step by step, the twenty

Dynastic frescoes, each linked to its following Palace.

And with determination, do not rely on any organized 'effect'; not one of those fugitive mirages with which western 'perspective' makes play and defines without hesitation: whether parallel lines join or not at infinity ... (wretched infinity where two lines are reduced to one point): if the personages drawn here have one dimension in space, or two or three ... (bah! that's something for a competent tailor!)

My role towards you is other and to these Paintings: it is to make you see them, only that. They are spoken Paintings.

Do not believe these to be words without any justification. Even the most ancient and classical Paintings, in the calligraphic and literary Empire, are not at all in agreement as to their purpose – which, above all, is the perpetuation of ignorance. But before ceding its colours, each has already stimulated its gloss: the margins are full, in an elegant style, with descriptions, commentaries, lyrical effusions. A carapace of words has been created. These Paintings are well and truly literary, as I promised in the dedication. Imaginary, as well.

... You are not upset? Sincerely, you did not expect a representation of things? Behind the words I am about to pronounce, there have been objects from time to time; symbols sometimes; often historical ghosts . . . Is that sufficient for your pleasure? And even if one did not find any images at all really painted on them, so much the better, the words would create an image, more freely!

And I am unable to dissimulate any longer: I call on you as indispensable helpers in this substitution. This is not written to be read, but to be heard. This is not made complete by being heard but demands to be seen. This is a shared task: on my side, a kind of parade, a display, a patter . . . . But totally useless, out of place and completely absurd, if it did not find in you its echo and its value. Hence, a *certain* attention, a *certain* acceptance on your part, and, on mine, a *certain* cadence, an abundance, an emphasis, an eloquence are equally necessary. Agree to these double stakes. But, before beginning to play, an anecdote:

– A Master-Painter, in the Sung era, had the habit of climbing up the terraces of vineyards, equipped with a flagon of wine, and of passing the day mildly drunk, staring and meditating. Do you know what he observed? Clearly a spectacle, since he was a Master, and a Painter. The commentators say: '*That he looked for the bond of light joining ultimately once and forever joy and life, life and joy*', and they mocked him for being a drunkard and a lunatic.

And yet, this inebriated vision, this piercing gaze,

this clairvoyance can replace for some people – to whom you belong? – all the reason of the world and of the god.

I invite you then simply to see. I ask you to forget everything about you; to hope for nothing further; and to regret nothing.

*
* *

. . . I hear you. Mere contemplation is not enough. But adventure, is it not too the joyful act! Be reassured: the spectacular action I laud is not a state of inertia, nor of beatitude: you shall experience that it is full of varied activities – some entirely unreal, but operating through the Spirit; others traced back very far through the journey; the last leading through four thousand well-counted years of Chinese Chronicles! Already, if you read such a thing in the introduction of a book (a book fashioned out of pages to be turned and of characters one skips when bored), do you not sense you are embarked on an unusual voyage, and already, gentle readers, do you not have a certain *laissez-aller* towards the author, even a taciturn one? Allow yourselves then to be amazed by this which is not a book, but a saga, a summons, an evocation, a *spectacle*. And soon you will agree that to see, as is the crux here, is to share in the Painter's gesture as he draws; it is to *travel* in pictorial space; it is to assume each of the painter's actions. Many among them will seem noble to you, in the sense that both criminals themselves and the masses give to that word. Some shall appear abominations in the judgement of so-called good men. Having listened to me this far, you no longer have any possible way out nor retreat but that which separates the good spectator from the spectacle. Didn't I warn you? There you are now my accomplices, my fellow conspirators. You may see them all, from now on. Look then: I unroll the first of these Paintings, the First Magical One.

I
MAGICAL PAINTINGS

And, in a trice, here we are catapulted into the ether, in the heavens. Clawed roofs toss Palaces into the ether. Rocks overhang roofs and climb up again to the ridge-pole before touching *this* beam from which the entire Painting hangs, descending right down to the terrestrial mountains, right down to hollows peopled by human valleys. But, between heaven and earth, a losenged esplanade proffers its shore for unreal landings.

For, in each quadrangular space, you see but one flight, without number, of those magic white birds. They are well-feathered arrows, steely-beaked, with red and delicate feet: they are well-mounted arrows: each carrying aloft one of those old men with humped foreheads, with rosy cheeks seen against chalky beards, with undulating robes unfurling in their wake; and each old man and his steed are but one: he, flying with its wings; it, guided by a stroke of his thought. From one small ethereal island to another, they come to alight on the white terrace, losenged, held up by a colonnade which you now perceive.

And right down at the bottom, here at the bottom, see that it is the fluid sea, its lappings represented by those thin undulations. It is from her, base of the earth, that this vertigo streaks skywards. Do you not find 'the point of view' immensely high? In the middle of the Sky! This is not painted for the use of mortals in their prayers and supplications, this is neither an ascension nor an intercession. This is inhabited only by Genies stripped of their human chrysalis. A celestial Painting. If you can see it with such facility, it is through the Painter's magic, providing you with this lofty crest, this domination of summits? Here one mounts the celestial geese and travels only by the road of the air. Do not look for well-emphasized lines: no starting point, merely a delicate ending. No bodies whatsoever! Glorious Spirits. A frail and immortal life. Of those beings which have nothing of old men except the beard and the pink gourd-like brow, there are easily a thousand, and more.

*

*   *

And now, whether the décor is solid or not, whether this esplanade (you see it losenged and white, carried by its colonnade) turns out to be of alabaster or of jade, or sculpted from words or a dream . . . do you find then it has any great importance? A great difference? The Spirits blow and reign everywhere He wills. This is a painting of Spirits, of Genies, of Immortals. All that is painted here has nothing concrete but its acceptance to be seen. All this deigns to appear. But know well, with one puff, all this can vanish. Those old men, we guess what they represent: the glorification of durability. They are the old sons of Emperor-Time.

And with age, you well know that every soul increases: that each intelligence exaggerates and spills over its station: the soul of an ancient bell goes back to that of a young tree: the soul of an old tree fans out further than its dry branches: the soul of an old animal thinks equally falsely as that of a wise man. The soul of an old man who has known how to amass the years over a long period of time – as others copper coins – penetrates souls and men, takes flight and comes to flutter about here in the quivering circle. Let us recognize the truly magic power of unique longevity.

Do not be appalled by the necessary attributes: the wattles hanging under the chin, the pouch-shaped belly. All that is scarcely visible under the ritual robes. And what need for youthful muscles? These old creatures have a noble bearing. Whether bandy-legged or one-eyed, they possess the air for their chosen path: winged chariots, the quick rhythm of a flag slapped on both sides and which vanishes: that is the method of transport in the intelligent azure: all is full of fluid like a throbbing ship: all shifts: the Heavens flap!

*

* *

Look again. After a little while, you might wish to see no more. You might prefer to wipe your eyes . . . (a magic mist). Each of the figures even when hurled ten thousand feet in space is defined, posed, complete. But the problem proceeds exactly from that which you now understand: namely that all this is in flux and all pulses in the most monumental indifference. The genie could equally well quiver madly in one sense as in the other. The esplanade is ready to rocket about as well; the crags to dissolve into the ether. All could be turned topsy-turvy; nothing would be changed: those old men shall become children and those babies old men. All is one. Two is not two. All dances, all sparkles; all is ready to twist into a helix (like the great wind of the universe). All is conveyed then by the spirit.

And think clearly, this Painting, having dripped off the brush of an old master of the T'ang era, is by its very definition spirit.

Seen enough. Let us unroll the second one . . . (Ah! I forgot to read the final pictograms glossing the First Magic One. Is it really necessary? This is called

RONDE DES IMMORTELS.

Now, the Painter offers here the image of a single young girl. She is beautiful in her beauty, long hands, plump neck, coiled plaits of hair, and the slant of her eyes. Another, on another place far off, truly exists, who resembles her. For this is a portrait.

The Painter renders her here more soft than the other is soft in real life; for he has painted her as he loves her. And as the other does not love him, imploring the image every day with words and with tears, he takes up a hard stylus and punctures the heart on the silk.

At that same second, in her house, the other emits a cry and clasps her hand to her heart. The mother panics about the house, for the girl pines away and nobody knows which doctor to call. Before long, she will surrender. It is the Painting which shall die; not the other; not the other. But the Painter then will no longer love her: this is a

FAITHFUL PORTRAIT.

And over there, there are more Genies, this time in human scale and five in number. The five robes swirl symmetrically. Gusts of wind play about between limbs and robes. The ankles move. The nails are iridescent. Can you not hear breathing? They seem to be benevolent. They are full of intelligence and know what we ignore, but ignore what we are. – Very far from us . . . On the other side. – Nevertheless they are alive, are they not? (A magic life.) They would be completely alive – you add – if their eyes had, like a well, that highlight in the iris?

Exactly. That is why I do not dare paint it in and would never do so: lest I see them abruptly surge out off the wall and mix with us living beings.

Let them remain then the

FIVE BLIND GENIES.

And what do you see that is so extraordinary? Why are your eyes heavy and locked on to this ... which is a human figure and nothing more? Seated within himself, sagging from head to knees: a Hermit a little bored with thought, doubtless, and nothing more.

Following a good old painterly habit, there is a wider space on the side where he stares out (so that his gaze does not come up against the void too quickly ...) But his gaze is precisely empty, dried up like a puddle in the sun ... Like yours at this moment.

And so what do you see then that is so extraordinary? It is a man, or it was a man, and nothing more. – However, he is not alone. In the top right hand corner, up there, right up there, another vanishes in infinity, another prances on the spires of gutted smoke – look carefully – gutted even of the skull of the exhausted one. A symbol, and nothing more.

But whence comes the panic in your eyes? – Ah, that, on the left shoulder of the figure in meditation; that which croaks out of the depth of shadow; that thing with eyes more bulbous than the forehead, and a neck pleated like that of an old woman; and you can distinguish that hand with four fingers which clasps the skull over-porous with intelligence, and which defines it . . . and from one corner to the other of a lipless mouth, that long laugh drawn with maestria . . . Is it that which frightens you? That thing? that?

A toad. A toad, I tell you, nothing more.

No epilogue to this Painting, the fourth of the Magical Ones . . . But yes, if you look carefully:

TRIUMPH OF THE BEAST.

Wait, before approaching the fifth . . .

(Is there any among you whose profession is that of a cut-throat, flayer, dealer in flesh who has lived? Is there one in your group who has snuffed out the life of a living being? Is there among you a fisherman with bow and arrow, or hunter with harpoon? Has any one, with a slash of his nail, sectioned the silken thread of palpitating hours and quick instants which follow one another like manacled breaths? Has any one drunk without a filter? Has he walked without lightening his step on the dust . . . perhaps in agony? Finally, is there any one among you who is not clear of all murder; even a secret one, even forgotten, even immeasurably tiny, ignored?)

If yes, let him turn away his eyes from this. For this depicts the Redeeming Hell of the Monarch of the Law, of Buddha, whom it is agreeable to make a god, instead of a Sage – and the abominable expiatory sufferings. He, who has stolen away life, shall see his own posthumous life writhe here in atrocious knots of entrails . . . Let no one among us take that risk: Who could pretend then to be pure in the eyes of his Law?

And yet, the inscription was welcoming, full of grace and promises:

HELL THE REDEEMER!

The Painting that follows is not one which hangs vertically, but should be spread out with a flick of the index finger and the thumb, like a semi-lunate fan carried in Spring and in Autumn, and is entitled, in fact, thus:

FLYING FAN.

Never let it rest: do not try to examine it flattened out nor to count the number of ivory ribs which structure it; but always give it its movement: fan the air and subreptitiously, out of the corner of your eyes, at each gentle gust it sends forth, look and, little by little, guess at the furtive scenes: the background is black and shiny. Suddenly, a segment opens: wings beat; large eyes roll: a skull is punctured: from it springs a pagoda which blazes across the open sky in one spout . . .

You saw? Fan, keep on fanning.

A personage takes shape: a naked monk, in ecstacy. Of his entire body, only two eyes remain, but how vivid. (The rest is desiccated or rotting.) He gestures that, on its own, the play is a good one. Fan on, fan.

Here only a gaping face greets you; so full of magic and so profound that it will latch on to your face and become *your* face, if, still fanning yourself, you do not change it into something which does not collapse; the curved line of the Painter's horizon; the mammoth undulation of the sea; the slow wing beat of the great pink goose in the sky; the composed, stark caress unfleshed of all desire . . . Fan on, fan . . .

But the painted face insolently re-evokes itself and defines itself at each step. It looks from too close up. What does it wish to say? Is it you who provokes it? To meet it out of this context: what a ghastly adventure! As the sight of an over-insistent friend, as a too clinging guilt, like a dumb person who wants to ask questions.

But we do not inhabit the real world. Whatever displeases or disconcerts us, we can, better than guilt, evict it, and with a simple movement of the finger, efface it.

Shut then your fingers: in a flash, the face exists no longer . . .

. . . An Emperor, dressed in red, stretched out on a vermilion bed.

The face and the eyes turn red; the pupils are flecked with sparks; and he stares with the smile one has for the Unique one whom one awaits and who is nearby; and he tosses before him his two warmly coloured hands with the gesture one makes towards the sole object one loves and which is there; and his neck, thrown back, burnt by reddish flashes, and his lips illuminated with fever, the entire Personage, richly painted, lights up and surrenders as if to a passion for something which we, however, do not see: unless – looking very carefully – plumb in the middle of the shining eyes: *a flame.*

But follow the stare: it goes directly towards that other small red flame which stands proud and unflickering in the night . . . Without a lamp and without oil, without any trace of nourishment save that dredged up out of the surrounding gloom. Yet it stains all with its colour.

It is that then! The Emperor yearns for that flame: he knows exactly what it is! He invokes and conjures it, he never quits it for a second with his eyes . . . And you too, look, look more carefully (from closer up, from inches away, being sure to hold your breath to avoid making it quiver . . .) It swells, it changes, it rears up, bends and twists around itself . . . Its tip splinters into a thousand hairs, and two long arms with etiolate fingers; its belly forks into two legs shimmering where they join, and it forms two breasts as well, blazing in colour, and lips, a tongue, eyes . . .

Is it still a flame? Ah! you can relax and breathe now . . . (if you can . . .) It does not flutter. It is man-sized; it splutters with the joy of consuming; it boldly triumphs; it is new, and, each night, resurrected: in its light how hard or soft or banal appears to be the concubine made of meshed flesh and blood! Next to it, what can his well-guarded girls, ripe with ritual, give to the sovereign Lover since he holds here and vibrant with life this Painting: this

MISTRESS FLAME,

blazing red, which licks him, surrounds him, penetrates him and melts down joy like a bronze cast into the heart of the furnace! Look! Look! He is eaten up by love of the flame.

But take care, hold your breath . . . In a flash, it shrinks to nothing, flickering and merely luminous . . .

No! No! Do not blow on it! – Even though that is what a wife frustrated of carnal love would do here. The Other, the Red, would go out and never more could be lit.

What follows is yet another

REFLECTION IN THE EYES

of a young girl, of course – that hairstyle and that posture! Those very eyes looking straight at you and me . . . or perhaps over our shoulders, into the space behind us? (Do not turn round.)

That face shows no signs of emotion. The delicate brow is polished; the eyebrows serenely curved; the eyelashes do not flutter; the wrinkles around the nose do not crinkle, nor do the lips clamp tight or open voluptuously . . . Look again: that chaste vaulting of the shoulders, and the hands folded against the stomach modestly as they should be, as if for a greeting she is about to give, or to conceal the obtrusive shame of marriage. In short, towering purity.

However, you might wish to know what mirage or train of thought gives that entire young body such a discreet bearing . . .

Well then! Look at her, directly in the eyes, as she appears to look at us. – If the Painter is on a par with the Masters (with the one who, in the pupil of the herdsman's eye, compressed the perfect image of the bullock with its spotted hide and halter), if the Painter was painstaking and keen-eyed, the REFLECTION IN THE EYES should encompass all they perceive and dream of. Concentrate on them then, from close up . . .

Oh! That meticulous, wonderful mirage, magically compressed into the small gleaming shield! One can discern there, as the commentary goes: 'two girls naked from their toes to their breasts, one on the other's knees who cradles and caresses her with her fingers'. (You can even make out the fingertips!) What conscientiousness in the Painter's vocation! It is then the action which the pure face reflects and contemplates decorously.

But however the eyes are locked with ours. So the reflection, where does it come from?

From *ours*? From that *space* behind us?

Do not turn aside then. Look at what is before you: a huge vista, a

LANDSCAPE,

the first among the Magical Paintings to be unrolled until now, of which it is the seventh. And yet in China, poets drunk with the brush qualify themselves as above all observers of the land. They have grasped its meaning. They have received its vision: they have kept its surface on the surface. And here is what they have seen:

Not much sky, and a great deal of earth. Piles of hills which are the work, and the witness, and the labour of the earth. Clouds falling from the sky both piercing and raising the solid revetments of the hills. The plain, simply tolerated, sapid, necessary: it is worked over, sown, harvested, but rarely painted. No man here, or merely the bare minimum to give an idea of human scale. But do not conclude there is a deficiency, or even worse an incapacity to paint one's peer or his portrait: it is yourselves, Spectators, you who should, more than a mime on stage, play the role of mankind here: and in such a way:

That the little which rests of the sky should garnish your brow. That the mountain's back should come and apply its great mask to your eyes. That the twin mountain faces, perfect for echoes, should muffle up your ears. There are no other men but you? But the landscape, truly contemplated, itself is nothing more than the skin – holed by the senses – of the gigantic human facies.

And now, here comes an entire

FEAST AT THE COURT OF A MING PRINCE . . .

and which is spread out over twelve large panels of a screen, taller than a man with his arms upstretched. And perhaps you would believe at first in the fortuitous swirling grouping of these hundreds of people colourfully encrusted in a black background? Follow then these two guidelines: The first, which begins in the extreme bottom right-hand corner and goes up to the top left-hand one. It is the axis, the vertebral chain, the great median honorific way. The other, which shadows it in an acute diagonal, stamps with its parallel lines the non-fugitive perspective, and gives free access to the interior of these imaginary palaces. It is so that, from near or far, one's footsteps have the same length, our heads, above, the same lintel. In this isometric space, freed from the terror of being brought up short or squashed by the foregrounds, freed of the 'point of view', even in the distance preserving our height, we are able, as we watch the feast, to take our part in it on an equal footing with the guests and with the Prince as he receives his guests.

*

* *

Let us allow ourselves to be led by the escort of this foreign Lord, who, right at the bottom, in this corner, on the right, comes around the ramparts, crosses the bridge, enters into the keep. Riding a pale horse, hidden behind a large fan with gilded rosettes, he orders the central gate to be opened, and strides between the two lines of welcoming musicians: in the bottom left-hand corner, trumpets, and, symmetrically, flutes and drums. We cross the vertical line of the two tall cinnabar-red poles, so high that the eye must follow them to the end in order to realize their use: they are the standard-bearers of two mighty Generals: the Western one goes and hangs its fanion over the musicians of the West. The other masks its lance point in the ether. Let us pass through the doors and the courtyards: here is the staff to greet us; we shall proceed, overtaking with our eyes the solemn Lord, free and buoyant towards the Prince.

Furthermore, if we so wish, leaping across the main roof with a glance, we can even occupy without indecency the area reserved for Princesses, concubines, attendants. As the outer court enjoys the feast, all those in the reserved enclosures joust and sate themselves with games. Ceremonious women friends come and exchange delicacies and greetings as they elegantly manipulate their dresses with powdered trains. And then, we cross other courtyards and gates, we leap over other walls. Here the corner where the children squabble, and, already well brought up, accomplish the same ritual gestures amongst themselves.

And in the distance, scattered among the lakes, but open to our view, small octagonal roofs protect two by two the lovers enamoured of secret music, shared in the sounding of the lute: in a poem offered and accepted, under the shelter of an insular kiosk . . .

*

* *

Do not believe in so painting, in regulating this space, in permitting thus a fragmented vision, do not believe that the total control is lessened. It is simple to find the reason, the crux, the axis of this feast, the focal point of this mass of five hundred figures . . .

It is not, as one might believe, the Prince himself,

seated somewhat heavily in his watered-silk red robe, and enthroned, majestic and replete, under the main roof... No! Seek out rather the exact point where the two main diagonals of the rectangle geometrically meet: not the spot which the Prince occupies, but the place he is looking at: two frail dancers facing each other at his feet.

The entire assembly, the whole spectacle, the organization of the whole feast comes then to alight on those delicate shoulders, on those two moving faces elongated by four huge feathers.

What is being readied has moving stage machinery. A sort of

THEATRICAL POSTURING.

Yes, I agree with you: the tonality is vulgar, like a trestle-stage with cymbals and coloured gongs! The stage machinery is equally crude as the hellish apparition and the fires and flames and smoke wreathing the genie, and the powder tossed into his face! – This depicts the story of 'the presumptuous man who wanted to fight at night'.

That is why, the entire back-drop is black; and why, alone in the middle of this blackness, there is a man, coiled up on one leg, eyebrows ferociously knitted, fist armed with a long horizontal sabre, preparing the blow he must deliver. Do not be taken in by his frightful aspect, nor by the borrowed flashy richness of his clothing . . . (it will be returned at the end of this play . . .) No matter, he is more of a scarecrow than a swashbuckling soldier of the Three-Kingdoms, and, coiled up on his leg, he does not stir.

You neither, do not stir: with one swallow take a very deep breath and hold it till you are exhausted: then the Painting well directed, like a simulacrum of reality, will unfold the whole pathetic vulgar tale – in the guise of popular heroics – which follows . . .

(But listen: before standing armed, alone, in the night, this man who seems terrifying and who is a traveller, accompanied by his women – a wife, a concubine – and by three of his children – an adolescent girl, a small girl and a small boy – in all five mouths and himself – this fellow arrived at the door of an inn which he had been told was inhabited by others other than men. He insisted on staying there. He was warned 'that he would not be alone during the night'. He went in, and as he splashed his face with warm water, demanded a sabre – he stood upright, examined it, and with a smile, wittily remarked: 'Simply let one ghost come then, I shall make two out of it.' And so there he is alone in his blackness, coiled up on one leg.)

No impatience: wait for the visitation. There! A tall Old Man oozing good manners . . . bows deeply before the man can unleash his arm ... and the blow whistles over his bent back. The Old Man stands up: 'My thanks! Mighty Hero! Son of Kouan-ti himself! In truth there are several ghosts here. That courageous arm has put them to flight ... My land has been freed. And I am the Genius Loci.' He turns pale, then dark, and before vanishing performs gestures which mean: 'If they come back, the others, do not forget to put that' (he points at the sabre) 'to good use.'

Once again the man is alone in his blackness, coiled up on one leg, sabre in hand, ready to slash into the night ...

Breathe in. Good. Look once more: the night is filled with people. It is no longer the Ceremonious Visitor but something ... a presence ... a face almost tangible and too soft ... Swoosth! With the blow, the sabre reaps a head which tumbles down and sticks to the blade with long glutinous hairs ...

Breathe in. Good. Look again. A new adventure: a confident smiling face . . . Swoosth! Second blow. – The face crashes down on to the flagstones. And three times over the identical movement: three, four, five. The last head is a small one, sliced off with the edge of the blade – breathe in deeply at last.

But here comes a smell or a colour no longer cold, but hot, then lukewarm, so that we are obliged to turn aside and flee, it permeates and revolts us. Take deep breaths: you cannot rid yourself of it: a smell! a colour! And yet he is there, the victor over the ghosts, always coiled up in the dark. Will he already scream victory? or rather will he, prudently, decide to wait for dawn?

Dawn breaks. Eyes drunk with daylight, he rushes outside, waving around, looking everywhere for his wife and his concubine, his two daughters and his son, to recount and describe his five combats.

Full daylight floods the stage. Everything is clearly visible: the five decapitated bodies can be seen, the five phantasmal balls, with their eyeless faces, their unpierced lips? Look harder: there are two pretty heads, intact under the make-up . . . And three more, all childish, all human. They are the wife, the concubine, the daughters and the son who came, prodded by the Genius Loci, an old vampire, and threw themselves under the blade. All can now be seen in full sunlight . . .

A crude day! I grant you: red and powder-white against smoky black. Jerky movements. It is commonplace, as so often life is, with its innate taste for the theatrical . . .

And yet, the following Painting seems to have but one desire, one aim: to become despite all a

LIVING PAINTING.

We see there an Imperial Chinese Princess, for political reasons turned into a barbarian Queen, surrounded by her children alien to her but hers. The costume details, the sumptuous and grotesque décor are scarcely worthy of our attention. Look rather at the face, classical and handsome according to the canons, and grasp what it signifies with a poignant touch which only occurs in this one Painting . . .

For she is riddled with internal tensions, hardly perceptible, but more moving than any gesture; the silk does not shift under the finger if you test it, and yet there are, in the waterings, throbbing folds like a caterpillar's back: the Queen formerly handed over wants to escape . . . from that country, or rather from her Painting. What sacrilege pinned her down thus between paint and silk, when Politics had merely locked her away in the barbarian provinces!

So this Painting is doubly an image of captivity. This Queen is the one who died in exile. When she was still living, one might have been able to try to free her, and, by opportune new treaties, bring her back inside the frontiers . . . But the brush, loaded with art and magical power, turned out to be more powerful and wicked than reasons of state. It has created her, immortal, bound, flattened on this thin fragile surface, animate, in agony as long as she is looked at. That brush shook with emotion and exuded the real business of life . . . And now, how to be rid of it? One hardly dares roll it and so incarcerate it in a cedar coffin as the others . . . To handle this throbbing presence as if it were paper? this imprisoned life which longs to be born? This breath which aches to be expelled?

The Painter, if he still saw her, would be aghast at his painting: she wants to be alive and is unable . . . Her eyes light up and veil themselves . . . She longs . . . – Oh! rather kill her! Kill this image in agony for so long. – But kill her then! She suffers without hope of any other human help but fire . . . Throw her into the fire . . .

Never more would she be seen in torment, with her grand royal bearing!

And this done, approach impassively the hard cold panel which I set up.

Here,

PAINTED ON PORCELAIN

under a thin glaze, here are tall women dressed in aubergine colours, with overcoats of a transparent green, and whose white-clay faces delineated by a thin red line simply depict good upbringing. The fabrics by themselves create the pose of a body delicately absent. These women play, with frivolous seriousness, at the tasks of the highest society. A few, with nothing to do, spikily lift up fingers with nails quick to stab a pin into their green-black hair.

And here are replete children, with round shaved heads, and a well-plaited *queue*. Here are civil officers at their ceremonials in ample green robes, offering to the beauties made-up with faces of cold moon, a raised brush which can project elegantly poems on the impassive white wall, or paint eyebrows on white foreheads.

There are symmetrical arches; palm-trees drooping like sleeves; phoenixes with lunatic plumage; blue storks; dragons whose bellies are divided into red and green, red and blue or yellow and red. There are horsemen frozen in a high-school gallop. A rotund emperor bent over violet battlements towards the departure of the chosen hero . . . who never leaves.

There are Sages, ghosts, infernal asteroids exploding like smoke bombs. There are the other world tribunals, underground, and their hidden games: the man spread-eagled naked between the woman's legs . . . All that, you Onlookers exiled from this décor, all that, not palpitating or gesticulating in our midst, but sheltered, very sheltered under the cold and translucent covering varnish, or well glued to the thin vitreous lacquer, both more reflective and crystalline . . . All that in a polished flat world, adamantine as tempered steel; a hard world, a world free from putrefaction, from deliquescence, brilliant: a porcelain world. Follow these insubstantial lines: feel these shallow enamels; see these brainless faces; glide over these breasts without relief; kiss these lips which do not respond; this hair which cannot be braided; these robes which cannot be stripped off... All that fixed by fire in a perpetual whiteness and an eternal transparence. This is a vitrified world: pain and pleasure cooked in the fiercest flames, and left to cool...

Are you jealous of this inalterable world?

If not, come down into the depths of

DEEP WATERS OF LACQUERS.

There is no more an impenetrable glaze: your eyes do not stumble up against a highlight, but are drawn of their own volition as if into the moving lakes of other eyes, they dive down . . .

Consider carefully that here nothing is brutally fixed in the mass: nothing here is abruptly petrified to ward off time. The surface is a smooth, viscous skin, which in addition preserves the memory of when it was sap and vegetable, and when it dripped, resinous saliva, from lips carved in a tree trunk. Varnish and balsam, spread coat after coat and brush stroke after brush stroke during craftsmen's long days and months and years, continue to live in there. Some of the original colours have become darker; they have foxed and vanished. Others which one would never believe to exist, emerge after a hundred years or so: they are those browns hatched by the passage of time: clearer and richer than the blacks: they swim up to the surface. Others roll around for a long time in mid-current. Heavy currents are present in this substance in osmosis, which never ceases to swirl, to filter, to dialyse . . .

And, bent over these waters, look carefully: here are the identical denizens to those of the porcelain world: once more you find those tall women and plump children: but here you feel that they are permeated by a graver existence. They move very slowly, that is true; but they sail on, they progress. Their gestures are dictated by the mysterious currents of balsam. And, just as in deep sleep, both feet and both hands and the shoulders, the knees and the mouth are glued together by the brown resin. They move so haphazardly that you would say that they have drowned, sucked down . . .

No. No. They participate in the life of essence and sap. Their mansion is a limbo darkened by thick opiums. They are drunk on their unguents . . .

You can be jealous of those ones without any fear of a brutal awakening: they sleep and live more insensately and more deeply than we do.

Do not retreat: do not throw yourselves backwards at the exit of this drop: do not attempt to interpose space between what you see and yourselves: come closer, as if from a parapet, to that which is a

FRESCO OF WOOL,

just as from a loved one whose touch is vital for the soul's and fingers' ease. Press your fingers and the thinnest most sensitive part of the wrist where the veins are . . . This is welcoming and soft; it is a stuff into which the palms, the elbows, the knees, all that is painful anywhere else – even sight – sink down and are at ease. To describe it better, I have stood this Carpet upright, stretched like a Painting.

It is not at all a Painting: and yet more richly toned and more dense in its dyes than many a panel of glued silk. Since you perceive on it the pile, with millions of small hairs, whose every tuft is a tuft... And above all, this Carpet has no 'theme'.

You are unable to discern any narrative on it. A descriptive Poet would be lost there. Tell them the following story: they are squares and angles; geometrical gestures; a survey of rational fields; no other movement is allowed; each line here is interrupted: see those large polygonal flowers in their reserved pastures like the prairies of inaccessible plateaux . . . An entire flowering herborescence whose style drily avoids any sentimentality. It is the triumphal quadratura of the living curve. You count on it the teeth, the segments, the chevrons of logical colours; right-angled areas under the domination of the weft (that pitiless canvas underneath, which is the stamina, the *raison d'être* of this carpet).

That is why I ask you to come closer and to touch. A carpet is knotted not simply to be looked at, but squeezed, trod on, penetrated up to its woof. And even further:

When you are totally exhausted or laid low by the porcelain technique – sucked down into the swamp of ruminant lacquers – when you feel bruised by the worlds which are neither of porcelain nor of lacquer but alive, come then and lie down as if in mourning on this carpet spread out on the ground. Come and smother in its pile the over-violent beatings of a heart which is yours, as well as the over-acidulous reflections in other eyes. Lie flat, in full human length, and forgetting nothing of its colours, sink in without thinking of anything else but cushioned rest in its wools.

Now, I must have you docile. I am taking you down an obscure corridor. Lower your head. Shut your eyes or not, as you prefer: you cannot see. Let us turn left. Go up these stairs. There are nine of them, in a spiral . . .

Raise your head: open wide your eyes; look into the depths of this gigantic basin of which you are the axis. These are, in their solemn order,

FOUR DIORAMIC PAINTINGS
FOR THE
NEOMENIAS OF THE SEASONS.

Look . . . I had promised you glued silks, complete panels, gilded rubbings at the ends of grottoes . . . but all by themselves the silks have ripped apart, the panels split; you will find no more surfaces nor known qualities in the colour scheme: nor porcelain-like – despite the brilliance – nor balm-filled despite the deep stretch of water . . . What do you want! To be enslaved? This is painted by the colour of the day and of the seasons: this is painted on a shifting sky by the signs of fine weather or of the storm. It is all which can be seen in the sky during the First Moons of the four Seasons.

Over there, first, at true North, at the extreme North, things in movement begin to swell. A wind one does not feel on one's face foreshadows the spurting of the thaw. Fish, flying in the aerial basin, come to the surface like divers and are about to crack open the thin shell. – Shadows of the migratory flight of the great geese.

Other movements froth: they are the hibernators who throb. – Snakes joyfully awakening at the sound of the first thunder! And tender green makes an appearance among the colours. Concentrate hard on this moment of the high clouds: from these wisps issues a blue-green chariot. The Son of Heaven, garbed in blue-green robes, adorned with green young earrings, has received from the Astrologer, measurer of time, the solemn pronouncement that Spring today manifests itself and enfevers this horizon of the North. The Son of Heaven of the High Clouds has left the Northern Palace. Drawn by six blue-green horses, he rolls over the eternal circular road. The

First of all men, ecstatic and quick, he goes to meet Spring. He charges off in his swirling smoke. He turns back and returns to the blue-green Palace, for here comes the time of the equinox. Look quickly at this moment, this point of balance: when day equals night. (– See all those busy people, fascinated by the sky, turning their heads upside down and their emblems too . . .) Weights and measures are verified in the Heavens; weights are weighed, hyper-sensitive bearings are regulated, as are flails, scrapers and rakes; and on those aerial canals, can you see, from down there, how the hull of the imperial barge is having its caulking checked by a transport minister? – All is got ready, is organized; but right up there, nobody takes the risk of harvesting. In the celestial countrysides, stallions and bulls are left free to pasture, let out into the blue . . .

And, remaining full of foresight, men dig out and drain the vertical paths linking the Sky to the earth, the riverbeds of plenty; the valleys of the zenith's springs. And one even takes shelter from the first annunciatory shower: do not anticipate the labour of Summer: if you do, plagues! Armed brigands! Insects falling in the place of raindrops and devouring the heart of the cereals! Do not anticipate the spectacle: the ceremonious contemplation of Spring should take place in amazement at its youth and at its unique and new novelty!

But, despite you, the horizon spins... The weather has changed and progressed, and suddenly, in his first

NEOMENIA OF THE SUMMER,

the Red Genie breaks out dense as a typhoon. No advance column: no escort and no cohort: here is the coming of the Summer. The Great Astrologer, during these days, has cried at the Son of Heaven in these terms: 'This day, Summer will show itself.' Here is the Summer.

That is why the Prince in Heaven, getting into his chariot, the colour of fire, drawn by roan horses with black tails, flanked by the scarlet standard, has donned his jewels, his red-summer earrings. Faster and hotter than terrestrial men, he descends to the depths of the Sky, he drives off to greet Summer.

Dive with his court into the hanging fields: feel how all the Empire and the blue firmament enrich themselves. Help is still provided for growth: but nothing can be altered: no great army is levied. The weather is good and heavy, propitious, swollen, full of sap, full of labour: the harvest inspectors are frantically busy: like a fine flock, with all its mouths, they see to it that the people have good pasture.

Here, you see medicinal plants being gathered. Here, you see the ambitious shoots sprout and increase . . . But look no more for the delicate flowers of spring's outset: they are dead.

In their stead, here is the approach of the Imperial First Wife. She is a lady with a red full face, fitting for the season. She is ripe and plump: she completes the education of the silk-worms: the cocoons are mature: one contemplates her, in this cloud, as she offers to Heaven that realized task.

And here, tossed around by the sky's smoke driven by Summer's breath, here is the orchestra of Summer, musical storms, the tempest, the crackling, the sharing, the bounties: the bowl of Heaven pours fire out from its ardent orb. And, from all its flagstones, its marbles, its allies, the earth, simulated up there by those white moving palaces, the heated earth sends back up the wind of its tepid breath. All around the sky of Summer, thunder's chariots gallop about in circles: heat paces its beat and becomes a leaden sound . . . Then, in accord with its tone, lutes' silks are tuned, drum-skins are restretched, mouth-organs are tuned and transverse flutes – in exchange, as an echo, in harmony:

Here is the reply from on high: see those beneficial arrows splitting open the earth's skin: see how the great rains of Summer pelt down, rich in genies and in males: see impregnating Heaven!

Then, one cuts out the gravid mares; the stallions are tied up. Soon the longest day of the year shall slowly pivot: life and death on this day have equal power. The Sage rests sagely in his house.

And repose falls also in this power! The stag sheds its antlers: the cricket begins to sing; a lukewarm wind rises. The young hawk tries out its wings. Rotting grass engenders glow-worms. It is the luminous moment: it is fitting to live truly in the heights of dense sky. It is fitting to gaze down on places from a vast expanse; to climb towers so high that one can pluck stars by hand. Everything swarms and multiplies: breathing is quick: you come to a climax.

However, the Painter of the Seasons in the highest firmament has taken great pains to represent here no other joys but those of the Summer; no other tasks but the tasks of Summer. If he had done so? Foul water, earthly water would have flooded the hills.

The harvests would never have ripened. The hawks too quickly would have gobbled up the young fledgelings. Hail would have come smashing down. Locusts would have scoffed up everything. And if, tempting fate, harvesting had taken place: each and every type of sterility would have ensued.

So, do not hope for more, do not seek to obtain more; but to be. To be, three times over to be, in the heat of Summer. To feel what one is. To know what one is. To laugh with pleasure at being, oh triple and triple glory of Summer!

But, despite you, the horizon revolves. The weather has changed and advances and unfolds high in the skies its third décor of the

NEOMENIA OF THE AUTUMN.

It is towards the western face of the earth that it is fitting to point your mobile human face: in front of the site where set both day and year; in front of the falling of the daily meteor. Let us follow it in its curve; let us curl up: let us feel on ourselves the weight of three seasons.

It is at that moment that cases should be judged, but according to the code, and heavy punishments fairly meted out: it is here at the height of Autumn itself that it is fitting to avoid excess.

Just instant! Harvested savour! The harvest is in and sampled. The Son of Heaven, that Mighty Mediator, samples in fact, prior to all others, and classifies all kinds of grain. – But first of all, he consults his Ancestors.

It is well like this that, without delay, without regret, or fevers or changing moods, it is fitting to accept and contemplate Autumn: but really grasp firmly the unique moment: do not delay your intervention: do not omit the gesture of sowing: cast the reddish stars over the field without heed or direction; sow the seeds under the open sky . . .

Turn finally towards the final quarter of the horizon. Each form and every semblance are mists, every colour dissolved but blue. It is a cavern of azure, a void separating heaven and earth, in accordance with this decree: That the emanations from on high stay on high, and may the effluvia from beneath never rise. That neither Heaven nor Earth communicate nor mate: that all the valleys remain closed; that there may not be one perceptible aspiration, not one foray into this blue, no thunder under this globe, no thought in the brain: let the Sage sagely abstain from action: no more desire and no more revulsion: alone, may transparence flow outwards – the crackling diaphanous in the dry air – alone, let pure blue, hard and blue blue reign.

By this standard, by this unfurling of the azure, you shall know that Winter arrives in his Kingdom in Northern China. It is truly him. What you have just seen is the first.

NEOMENIA OF THE WINTER.

What you are about to see at last is, on the other hand, irrevocably, the final Magical Painting.

And you will agree on your own that after this one, it is impossible to imagine one more – even one commissioned by the reigning Sovereign.

And yet, all there is at first is a large wall, of indeterminate colour, made out of bricks and rubble; with stains, incrustations, hoary growths, black or snowy moulds: one has the shape of a Palace roof – (follow the horn in the grey air); this other, accentuates the wake of a triangular flight; this other, an overhanging rock, and this one right in the centre, flat as the palm of a hand with outstretched fingers to receive, carried like an offering by these columns, haunted by genies – here is the losenged terrace, already seen, already recognized . . .

And all the upper reaches of the air are a flapping of prodigious white birds: well-feathered arrows, with steely beaks, with delicate red feet: each one carries its old man with his great bulging forehead: rosy cheeks, eyes pin-pointed with a magic dot, the beard and the robe slapping in the wind of the wake, but with nobility.

And right at the bottom, the sea of the abyss, vertiginous (if some man or other happened to be there and could take fright and fall). But those who travel on it are all Genies navigating along the pathways of the air. In this prestigious space, this wall as it is described is nothing else but – you recognize it – the First of the Magical Paintings; it is, once again, the

RONDE DES IMMORTELS.

Stroke by stroke, and almost word for word. The end is given at the outset, the final number is included in the first and that in the infinite. One is one. Even two is one if you so wish. Nothing of what you touch each day is solid. All that you have just seen exists, if you knew how to see it. But do not do as that somewhat illiterate Emperor of the SONG era, to whom the Painter boasted of this Painting and the others unrolled before it, and who began to sigh heavily.

In front of these Palaces in the stratosphere, in front of these accessible ravines, these haunted rock faces, these astounding palpitations, these pious tortures, these red lips and these loving flames, these landscapes gaping wider than any face, these demoniacal or gesticulating beings, these lives incarnate in silk, porcelain, lacquers or wools; the codified triumph of the four seasons in the sky, the Emperor began to sigh heavily. He deplored that none of them were in his domain, in his house.

Having stumbled on this vulgar urge, the Painter, unsmilingly, clapped three times with his hands. And lo, a door in the Painting, there – at the bottom of this wall – see how a small door opens there: look carefully at the end: a roads opens up right at the end.

The Painter said politely:
'May I be allowed to go first?'

And he goes, enters by the door, advances and climbs like the wind of an inverted fall . . .

And he becomes small; then: a dot. He becomes spirit and vanishes.

The Emperor immediately wishes to follow him and, in the same way, cross through the door . . . shut, erased. The entire Painting and the others previously unrolled have vanished. The wall once again is grey, stained grey, made of bricks and rubble.

The Painter alone and those who know how to see have access to magical space.

II
CORTÈGES AND TROPHY OF THE TRIBUTES OF KINGDOMS

A single roll of silk, scarcely as high as a forearm, but long – you shall see – longer than the famous landscape spread under the brush which followed the entire journey of the Great River; and longer than the interminable sequel to the Ten Thousand Genies, opening the door of the Palace of black crystal . . .

No! Do not unroll from top to bottom: this is no longer a Magical Painting, capable of being manipulated from top to bottom or upside down or towards the depths of the soul! Spread this one out from right to left, from one hand to the other.

Moreover, these four large characters, placed as an introductory inscription on the encompassing volute, are there precisely to warn of the nature, the value, the sense of the painted images which shall follow one after the other. They form a complete, well-balanced sentence which should be read:

CORTÈGES AND TROPHY OF THE TRIBUTES OF THE KINGDOMS.

It is then a *horizontal procession* of *precious* things, coming from *all over the earth*, going towards the *same* destination in order to form in the *same* place, at the feet of some One.

It is therefore also the Journey - power in wide spaces, the presence of what is not here, which comes from afar and which is sought after so far away: DIVERSITY - which is not that which we are, but other, giving to the extremities of the world that taste of another world - if this were possible over and beyond the too human Sky. It is the Journey.

Not in the high clouds - like the long heavy caterpillar drooling at each step, it is firmly fixed on the terrestrial plane. Recognize despite all artifice, despite all magic of the Painter in mid-movement of synthesis: the Open Space, he will reduce and condense it as air is vitrified by the alchemist in his furnace; you can manipulate it in your hands: you roll it from one to the other; you will pin down the fleeing landscape, and you will place where you will the realm of your sight.

Well then, whether or not all the personages here are in movement and march quickly, all these tribute bearers, sometimes well horsed, even so you will overtake them with the edge of your nails just as a honed spirit catches up with and precedes the passage of seconds. You will even be able to oblige the Cortèges to go backwards and the rivers to swallow back their springs . . . You will not do it! You will not retrace your steps; and you will not believe also in the faithful thrust of the past: it is in front, it is distance which is the tractive force: unroll them then without discontinuity from right to left: do not interrupt the procession . . . And do you know where it leads?

Towards HIM, Centre, Middle, unique son of the One-Heaven. – A voyage is a fine thing, indeed, but in principle taboo for the Emperor outside the palace of the Borders. This then has been painted to fill that gap; so that the ones on the outside and from elsewhere mass here and justify their absence. Just as an Edict, a few strokes of His brush, reaching the ends of the world are going to bring warmth and justice and satisfaction to all the subjects of the Universe – on the contrary, all that at first is distant, comes sooner or later, out of respect, by guile, by choice or by force, to join Him, to prostrate themselves anonymously in a single homage before HIM.

*

* *

That at least is the meaning of the Inscription, in a

fine cursive, which glosses the title and takes up the first fold of the tome. Unroll.

Two folds further on, you see nothing but a neutral field starred with splashes of gold which shall wash from your eyes domestic fogs and everyday sights . . .

. . . Here you are with the clear polished gaze of a mirror. See the colours, so consistent and so powerful in your well-prepared eyes, that they spill over the contours and the outline. They are frothy blues and greens, living turquoises, olivaceous fields, hillsides of blue ash: peaks delineated by curves more noble than the twin humps of the yellow camel . . . Unroll.

Under your left hand appear, shining against the green lining, splendid reds and this vivid ferrous metal colour: the stamp of man. Then these shapes not natural either: serrated lances, blades, halberds, a shaft without leaves tossing its tuft of wild hair . . . Both these toys and baubles go forward, carried by the swing of the movement, from right to left, always in the direction of your eyes. Unroll.

A wide ravine opens up. Here is the first Cortège which you pass one by one: horses, horses of so many breeds! But ten should be especially singled out: that black with black eyebrows, that rain-grey, two scarlet, a pale yellow, a peach blossom, the striped one, the dappled one, that scaly one and finally the last one with a shaggy coat like a bear. They are bigger than chariot mules. See that neck, and that plaited mane. See those chests and those rumps streamlined by the stretch of four legs in full gallop.

These animals are famous for their total disdain of the wind: if they do not overtake it, they weep, come to a halt, then go off again and it is said that they continue until they sweat blood. And they cover easily a thousand leagues, from dawn to dusk.

The men leading them, on foot to rest the animals, seem to be very exhausted, thinly attired despite the richness of their tatters, and carrying or dragging bunches of fruit said to provide a wondrous drink, full of flavour, of wisdom and hilarity . . .

At their head, a man haggard and harassed, leading the first tribute, Tch'ang-Kien, emissary of the great western periplus. He is on his way back from thirteen adventurous years. He is emaciated by the time passed, the force spent, the repetitive shock of distances – and his face is eroded by the brutal breath of glaciers. If you see him thus, painted before any other cortège, it is because he, the first, starting off from the Centre and bursting asunder the borders, 'broke the ice'. And since, the Empire truly communicates with those countries of harsh names: Baghdad and Ferghana, and that extraordinary Soghdiana, fatherland of fine horses, origin of wine!

The exacted tribute is doubled by freely given more

precious gifts: the Princes of another city under siege over there, its site unknown, have decapitated their king in order to send his head in homage – and that is why, by pictorial parataxis, you see Tch'ang-Kien clasp to his chest that round object, the size of a gourd, wrapped in a gold embroidered towel from which seep drops of blood – red and brown.

Before him, fresher than the horses, the bunches of fruit and the decapitated head, here comes, carried by four bearers in a litter, here comes the very Daughter of that Soghdian king. (Out of decency, you will never discern her features.) But she goes, mixing mourning with hope and tears with marching songs, she goes along, servant, concubine, or promised spouse... May the Sovereign, in the Palace of the Centre, deign to accept as is his absolute right the horses, the wine, the head and that one said to be extremely beautiful, but ashen with her complexion of the skin-of-death . . .

Unroll. This first tribute from the Marches enters into this mountain pass and disappears, feeling its way through a roadless chaos behind other tumultuous mountains . . .

Further on, these open up on to a dry river bed: fortuitous route, but imperial road, whose pebbles are slabs and large erratic blocks, watch-towers. Although foreign, these ones walk without a guide. They come perhaps from even further than the horses of Tch'ang-Kien; further away than Ferghana and Hira. They are the envoys of a petty ruler, Ngan-tong, or, as they emphatically pronounce: 'Marcus Aurelius Antoninus'.

They have round heads, short hair; and look at their large noses, their non-slanting eyes, truly too sunken, their strides a little too rhythmic. They wear short robes, have small carts; full hands – not with bronze coins stamped by a real kingdom – but with tiny coins they make believe to be of silver and gold – unpierced, impossible to thread in ropes. In their baggage, which they take care to leave visible, there are brocades fleshy as skins and other dry fabrics – one might pronounce mineral – which fire washes over without burning; there are red shrubs made out of coral; perfumes exuding an unknown scent; storax, which is the accumulated juice of a variety of virtue-filled plants with strong saps. They have carbuncles. They have amber, its pulp so soft and so light that in grasping it you lift it higher than you might have wished . . . and in which eyes drown . . . warm amber with honey cells . . .

If you follow them attentively, with their jugglers who spit flame, surrounded by sacks they willingly open by the roadside in order to barter, it is unclear whether or not they are porters accredited to embassies . . . or just very sly merchants!

Let them go anywhere in peace. They bear witness to the distant reputation and stories about the Empire. Let them go up to the Palace of the Centre where His gaze might find some amusement in their aspect; until the day, when, convicted of using false weights, forbidden trading, they shall bring to the deepest prisons the final tribute of their mingled blood and bones. – And let us rapidly leave them behind.

Let us catch up with these ones, who come from the South with its burning sun of Annam and the Champa country; winters where water is never ice-bound; where snow is talked of with disbelief and is preserved, if it falls, in precious small coffers. That is why you see them naked: puny too: not the flesh of the Hundred-Families. Those sunken eyes! that hair twisted up into chignons without pins! those rings in their ears! the neck weighed down with necklaces; wrists sagging under bracelets (since they do not know what to do with their hands), they playfully string useless bows; they blow into shrill conches and scratch the skin of their drums.

They would quite simply appear ridiculous if they did not lead, alive and puissant, those moving mountains, those grey creatures, born of the sun and heat: four legs, rounded and thick like temple columns, fan-shaped ears, a docile nose, stretched out two arms' lengths; those so-called 'elephants' can be harnessed with the utmost dignity to the chariot of the

Son of Heaven or – if He spurns them – would make suitable war steeds. Two of them, green skinned, are already armed with cuirasses . . . take note of that small gilded bag hanging around their neck.

It is battle balm. It is filled with human bile collected during nights of man-hunting: to ensure inevitable victory, the brow of these mighty beasts is rubbed with it, and suddenly convinced, amok, mad to crush and grind, they trot into the enemy lines, reaping heads like ears of corn, flailing with their trunks, on their hind-legs, they trumpet with joy.

And beside them, coming as they do from heat and sun, over-ripe palm trees sag and bend, exhausted, rotten with succulent juices fermented in the sap; flowers as enormous as the heads with flapping ears: armfuls of roots with a soporific taste. Amongst this unfolding which, going from your left to your right, weighs down that hand and lightens the other, a flock of women insinuates itself calling for their men – busy with very different types of games! Yet they go freely, as honest as fruits searching out mouths, covered merely up to their breasts, back and thighs entirely naked, desires to the wind. They attract no attention but yours. Hardly worthy to walk in this procession of homage, hardly able to be qualified as women in comparison with the lowliest wench in the ante-chambers of the Palace. In truth the road is long up to the emplacement of the Unique Master. They will be worn out and aged before they sully with their excesses the ceremonious parade of the Prince when he approves his concubines.

They hide in pairs under the stifling furs.

The mountain reappears and takes over. Once again, the curves of the mountain faces swing from one end to the other of the wide open space; then they rear up, fragment, and puncture the sky with their needles. There is no longer any practicable path; there is not even any possible path other than the furrows of the wind where the geese drive the plough of their triangular flight.

The surge of the hills spreads out; countries tense their spines. The earth swells. The air is refined. It is the sacrifice of the soil down there; it is also the ceaseless contribution of the heights: – like all things this is on its latent way towards Him. It is the water-tower from which the rivers, draining his provinces, flow; the solid storm whose waves advance to hem in his horizons. It is Tibet with its double offering. While the mass surges up, the moving trophy – clouds and quick waters and that mighty torrential wind sweep down and cascade over his Western Marches.

Unroll slowly: advance nobly like the caravans: like

these oxen wide-horned and clothed in long hair; like their drivers majestic in ample pomegranate robes. Their wide faces lacquered by the blast of a dense wind, their large caskets – where their holy things are kept – hanging down and flapping against their broad chests, they descend with raking strides that you could scarcely match. Do not attempt, even with your eyes, to resist, to climb back up. All comes from on high here, with the consciousness of the ponderous crystal of the glacier and the heavy might of the cold air.

They go on. Their unique shelter . . . tents of rancid colours. They prepare oatmeal gruel, having gathered, for the fire, dry dung. They whip and preserve milk, in order to skim from it a yellow grease which they prize highly – famished and needy enough to the point of milking female beasts!

For copulation, they have those women, little different from themselves, with wide antelope faces, braided hair, sturdy ankles and fat feet. – Are they proud then of nothing of all this? Is it because of nothing of all this that they walk towards Him, during entire months, on this reverse slope of the highest mountain?

To go thus is their property and their riches. Ready to fight, ready to sleep, ready to share fraternally the same married woman; ready to die a solitary death:

That is their secret tribute, this knowledge – the simplicity of the summits – that is what they carry with the fragrance of snows and air. That is what they are going to offer.

They descend. They pass. And no one could halt them . . .

A dark ravine full of night, criss-crossed by moving lights. Follow them, and not haphazardly: look more closely; each one goes forward over the two up-stretched arms of a man called: 'Branch-bearer of the sun.'

They hold in their hands these branches of the Jo tree and their orange flowers, reflections of setting suns. Held up very high in the sky and turned towards the meteor at the instant of its disappearance, these corollas soak up its colour, drink its fire, and continue to blaze. That is why, the 'Branch-bearers of the sun' go fast and surely in the dankest obscurity. Their faces which gaze on the flower shine forth like moons. That their steps are hindered by this lofty gesture, or their bodies deformed beneath oily garments, is of small importance: they possess these post-midnight stars: they despise and cleave the night. Follow them. – Do not desire that they lower – even for a minute – their tensed arms: at once, the flowers would go out!

Follow them. They are right, tomorrow, the day will reappear . . .

Day comes again . . .

A wide day, of troubling size: the sky is double: above and below are alike and the ground is missing under your feet. Unroll then abruptly what space there is between your two arms: then, move no more: there is nothing which should change in this isotropic horizon . . .

And yet, under your eyes, this changes its skin, colour, and mood: this has nothing to do with the trampled road. And yet, violated by ships' keels this is lacerated by nets, battered by oars, inhabited by myriads of beings as birds the wind.

This is more ancient and fundamental than the solid continent: It is the sleeping, weeping, voluble sea whose name we are about to read (that which so many travellers ignore) . . . But, neither the Gulf Sea where a voyage from one cape to another takes three days; nor the hot waters where fish flash like arrows and beat their dragonfly wings . . . Nor the Glacial Sea, which endures during the months of winter. This one is not cold and is not hot; tepid as the temperature of tears and storm rain. It is neither here nor there. You recognize it suddenly, before you, when you had hoped to have escaped it. It is the Sea of Immense Nostalgia.

Do not launch the junk at random, even if proven, there where your eyes sail. - You would like to dive in there . . . Reflect, and reply.

Above all, have you killed in yourself regret as countless as the quivering fish? (There is a passenger it cannot stomach.) Have you extruded out of yourself oblivion of all your women, and, of more than all your women, of that one who, not being yours, possessed you all the more? And cast to the winds tenderness towards children who, doubtless, will never be born: for one does not traverse this sea twice. And neglect the laudable urge to greet your parents later, to see again those puerile places which astounded your childhood. Haggling over your return, drown first of all, in the pure water, all desire to come back later, to do over again what you have already done.

If not, do not embark. - You still have, you believe, an acceptable counterbalance for renouncing the crossing: your packages: your cumbersome rich packages, an entire family sails with you! Take the land route, meticulously portioned out, and which, in addition, via long detours, leads more or less to the same goal. But do not drop the anchor of your eyes in the Sea of Immense Nostalgia. Turn away. Unroll. Reach the other side in haste. Land.

Find your way back to the extended road. Unsullied by any walker, the Road walks on beneath your eyes. Even deserted, it remains the perpetual site and the link of the cortèges. Numberless as the veins in jade and the mesh of the net of the firmament, so it weaves together the extended flesh of the Empire. Here, you see it narrow, harsh, vertebrate: lest it be submerged either by the rain or by the harvests (three harvests in four years). It is covered by slabs of soft sandstone, grey and violet, like the earth, springing under sandals' tread. A fine way for the incessant tribute, split in two, of the country of PA and CHOU, always advancing on the backs of men!

Follow the road: it widens and turns friable. It drowns in dust: it becomes indistinct and without edges in those northern plains where the Painter refuses to follow it . . .

Down there, tribute is carried in baggage-trains, or by the slow caravans of camels, beasts a little too slavish to be depicted here. Here, see the road at grips with the earth, the yellow cliff, and its castles and its breaches, its crests and its walls. The road becomes deep cut, and the plodding footsteps encrust it more and more profoundly. The road goes down into the earth. But the landslide of an entire hill cuts it. It must jump across and start again further on.

The road continues. The road never forgets its goal. Choked with mud, or paved, the road is prostrate in its length at the feet of the Master.

And those who swarm over it now at last can walk with elation. They are small, with flashing limbs. Their faces show a few common characteristics with the Sons of Han. But how much more puffy! Look then at those cheekbones! That badly placed hair covering the brow like a helmet! Where do they come from, with that mechanical gait, empty hands, and unbent shoulders? If they are asked what they intend to lay before the Emperor, no one replies. Beyond a doubt, they have not understood . . .

In truth, it is a very short time since they emerged from an era of original night. They are children without any inheritance, skilfully enriched by what they shall learn. Beneath their wooden temples, there is an ancestral ferocity. In the depths of their coal-black eyes, a fire glows, beneath hypocritical flames.

The leader, small like the others, repeats indistinctly a diplomatic formula he will recite at the feet of the Minister of Tributes:

'We are called "the Dwarfs"! Know that we come from puissant JAPAN which is a solar foundation. We carry nothing on our shoulders? It is because we come to learn all that is good for us, and to carry everything away with us.'

In fact, they walk in columns like good schoolboys. They truly deserve an audience and teachings.

They would continue up to the end, if the road, bogged down in this swamp, did not allow your eyes to overtake them briskly.

And the swamp divides into canals where lighters move – in long damp ribbons which men on foot, paid to haul on the tow-ropes, bestride with their trampings. It is so that all the filth, the puddles, the streams drunk up by the sands, all the waters one would call dead – putrefying – may join their reaches and drain the provinces into one network.

On it, more sluggish than the columns on the road, but capable and powerful, wend the flat boats laden with provender, perfumes for fragrance, fine rice, fat and white for the mouth. On it floats the pleasure fleet which the boatwrights of the South have sculpted for Him out of varnished tree trunks, free from decay and light on the water. The crews are alert for any turbulence. There are more than five hundred men, well dressed from shoulders to belly, thighs unencumbered so that they can walk when necessary in the water and on the sand.

Following on exactly one after the other, from the

last to the first, you can count: the kitchen boat, the Officers' boat, then that of the Councillors. That of the Eunuchs, that of the blood Princes. The winged vessel of the Princesses, the Phoenix-Nest, the abode of the twin Empresses. Then come the armed junks, and finally the Dragon-Vessel, which is for Him.

So long, that it can hardly be seen entirely between your two hands! So tall, that the fourth roof takes its wake into the high clouds, which flow astern as the cleft waters around its breast! The hull is yellow and scaly. The tail is furled and carries the superstructure of the poop over the tiller's mess deck. The captain whom all obey is this insect clinging to the scales – underlining, by its diminutive size, the vastness of the watery Palace. There is a moderate breeze, blowing North towards the Capital; the ochre sail woven with losenges has been hoisted aloft. The mast, lacquered red, bends elegantly. The warpers run along the bank to avoid being left behind.

Quickly, you too, to avoid being left behind, unroll: do not halt at this scene where the water level drops or the banks narrow, where one sees the rising filth and the feet, just wet, sink into the mud.

If by chance, through the jealousy of some god who regulates the canals and the flumes, there was not enough water under the broad keel, the yellow Boat would know how to sail on even so: all his tributaries one after the other, hundreds of grain-laden barges would spill, under its sides, that harvest of their sides: the Dragon-Vessel would make its way on the cereal ocean.

And the other, the Dragon, would float equally light on this creeping fog which envelops us – (is it the exhalation of the canals and the swamps? The breath of already dead waters?) This vapour is like those mists which accompany or hide those beings one cannot call 'human', despite their sometime human physiognomies. It is the breath of a spirit, lost amid the ponderous offerings from all sides . . . A sort of intellectual Tribute!

Do not be taken in! Do not let yourself be blinded. Endow your gaze with the piercing quality of the small eyes of Great-Flexibility: cut through this fog. Rend and tear apart the grey shreds . . .

Discover yet more colours, banners, standards, and suddenly these reds and this gold flitting through the wind. Look at this embassy: or rather, swaying high over their heads, look at these images: an almost naked man, hanging from both his outstretched arms, the face framed by a great gold roundel which forms a full glory. Bent before him, look at these monsters with gentle faces – difficult to say if male or female – downcast eyes, covered by jejune eyelids: the hands joined and pointed, enormous goose wings attached to both shoulders and their brows radiating fire!

Such are the mobile banners of a convoy inexplicable if inscriptions, here and there – which can be read – did not proclaim 'religious'. You have to believe in the merits of what they preach, as the stuffs and the embroidered emblems are sumptuous: and this troop does not progress in the confusion of highway robbers.

As for the porters, messengers, or adepts, they seem to be rather badly dressed in sackcloth and mud. They move forward, talking, teaching, prophesying. They claim to do nothing other than reveal these images and words, to comment on a well-known emblem: CHE, 'ten', whose cross-shaped characters have perhaps a new significance: the power of a pact, an alliance . . . the tribute of a god newly born?

Deign, deign, Son of the Sky, to accredit that one too among the rest.

Here is the halt: in one flash the landscape splits in two: a tall dry cliff rises up from the plain, and, crowning the crest, ten thousand, tens of thousands of Mongol hunters, upright in their saddles, halted on the edge of the obstacle, look over and observe . . .

. . . observe with all their lustful eyes. They come from the North, Land of Grass and Cold: you feel it, all of them have on their skin from birth the smell of their horses' manes. All in cuirasses of iron-plaited leather, ready to flee and to attack, they have just come to a halt there, on the edge of the void, and they project their ravenous hunger over the plain spread out beneath their feet.

It is not possible to call these ones 'vassals' with any verisimilitude – devastators of cities which, called on to surrender, refuse. – And yet, by their raging obstinacy, by their passion to conquer the well-surveyed foundation of the Empire, do they not bear witness of their own accord that they possess nothing, these coursers of the earth, if they did not first hold this Flower of the Middle?

For it is it, for it is the Empire, for it is the land they lust after which stretches out beneath their feet. It is for it that they have left behind their family clans and the pastures of the ancestral horde. Their covetousness, suspended up there, is it not in its way the most extraordinary homage? For the Empire, conquered by them, will then absorb them bones and all. They will learn its language, its habits, its lightest customs. To it they will make a holocaust of their entire martial power, of all the blood of their tribes, countless, untamable.

Is it not the most obsequious of tributes which these proud brigands from the North have in their possession to give?

But, with your gaze, leap over the cliff. Fall into the middle of the plain, at the springing of the arch of this elegant bridge, circular, reflected in perfect symmetry in the canal.

And in the air, in the water, in space, in the image of the bridge, a circular hole forms both a resting place and junction within the Sky. (Which demonstrates that, despite all haste, you must not dash in a tumult towards Him.) Whatever the necessity, the Tributes should slow down here, space themselves out, put themselves in order, rise up in turn on the plump back of that convex road, make a circle, touch the Sky and finally debouch . . .

(Unroll, unroll quickly right up to the end . . . at the verge of this hemicycle, shut in on the right by the cliff we have already seen, open on the left to all the horizons of a sea. – In the middle, suspended between the dais of an antique sky and the squamous grey of the sea, a terrace, nine times multiple, supports at the top of its eighteen steps:

HIM, SON OF HEAVEN,
SOVEREIGN-EMPEROR.

You see him! You are allowed inside. You have an audience. Discreetly you glance about over what is around you . . .

He does not look out towards the sea: but from the height of his shore detached like a peninsula on the architrave of a continent, he condescends to contemplate the Empire in movement, the Earth whose offering he is about to receive. Attentive to the splendid arrival, he is thus isolated haughtily. Only the homage, like a breath, shall then rise up to Him alone. The Tribute plodding heavily along the roads, here is the site which, suddenly, contains it: here is the tray of offerings stacked with all that was unrolled, passed in review, scrutinized one by one, and there is no need to paint it again so that it is repeated here, swollen with colours, piled up, banked up:

– The superb horses from the country of Soghdia; the head of the king and the girl; the vine and the wine; the western trash; the elephants and those sunflowers and those sun-filled corollas despite the night: all the daily provender which each Prefecture, each district, each small valley knows how to produce in its season and in its climate, and also the bizarre offering of a new god making his way to pay homage to the Son of the Being who encompasses all the gods, celestial functionaries, just as he governs humans.

Finally, finally here is the Other, in which the brush delighted:

So beautiful that one cannot look at him without weeping: so rare that he is thought to be unreal, the *Unicorn* himself, of his own volition, comes to mingle with all the promises of happiness for the people, witness of merits for the Emperor, and dances at His feet in an elegant dressage step!

He is alone, between Heaven and Water, his face turned towards the Earth, the visage round as the visage of a Immortal. On the outer and inner garment, there are the twelve emblems affirming possession of the World: from top to bottom, from tunic to skirt: Sun and Moon; Stars: Hills; Phoenix and Dragon: Vases; Algae; Flames; Axes and the Principal Characters.

It is Him. Admit that He is unique under the Heavens which he joins with his head to his feet on the Earth. What Sovereign was ever thus at one and the same time man and sacred?

It is truly Him – and all moves to recognize it. Him – not one Emperor or another, but this singular successor elected by the mandate of Heaven; this Present Day with tomorrows obscure or full of light! Regent whose name stamps the reign; link in the dynastic chain! So near and close to his people that he is obliged and must devote himself, even accepting lightning and rain and opprobrium, in exchange for the unique happiness of this people; so high in the vertiginous Sky that he ducks his responsible head into it and reunites as mediator the two Principles which mesh through Him.

*

* *

And here, in one TROPHY, here before Him, the provinces, the roads, the Marches of the Kingdoms, the boundaries and reverse space, the Underbelly of the whole Sky.

May the Unique approve the Diverse, and without mixing taste the strong saps.

May the Master approve his vassals and make a sign which allows all which precedes to exist

– or else, reject it . . .

III
DYNASTIC PAINTINGS

Mencius says:

That the Sage and very official Saint, Patron of Teachers, Moderator in the pay of Princes – Confucius, from the country of Lou – walking one day, one foot decently after the other, in the old palace of the Tcheou of Lo-yang, modestly raising his eyes to the walls, perceived the painted figures, as if alive, of the good Emperors, Yao and Chouen, and of the Great Yu first of the Hsia. The master, paying homage to the images with moderate delight, manifesting a joy which avoided extremes, giving a true teaching, the Master said:

'There is how well-governed houses begin!'

'There is how families are founded and clans increased!'

But, having arrived further on face to face with paintings of tyrants deemed vile, abruptly he walked off obliquely, averting simultaneously his eyes, his movements and his spirit, discreetly fleeing the supreme examples of infamy, and controlling his revulsion.

Then he walked off, followed by his disciples, in a still measured gait, the left foot leading.

*

*   *

Neither the Master, still less his disciples, you may be sure, would stoop to compromise themselves with us and would not have adequate disdain towards the spectacle which I claim will enchant you. They are not the Good Emperors I am commissioned to paint here. Let us greet them, as we pass, gripped by historical respect. Let us come to a halt in front of the others.

The others, those ruinious ones, those destructive ones, the Ultimates of each dynastic fall, those wicked Sons of Heaven who go, '*belts loosened, by revolting paths*' . . . you will agree that they are no less worthy to be seen, since they are no less necessary! The First Ones are lauded, called Founders, Renovators, Law-Givers, Mandatees of the high and pure Lord-Heaven . . . But how then can one renovate, how to restore order without first of all installing disorder? How can justice be admired and stimulate fine deeds for its sake, unless from time to time Injustice reigns dancing on the world? How can the Mandate be obtained, unless contrary precursors, devoted beyond death, even as far as posthumous contempt, prepare the obverse of the task?

The First Ones created the Empire and welded its dynastic chains; – sometimes it was necessary to reforge the links with red-hot steel. Let us render honours and justice at last to those whose successive perditions brought forth so many renewals.

So it is them alone we shall contemplate. I promise you a varied spectacle. They do not perform a play of virtue well learnt; no Book either teaches or permits any one of the actions they execute. Gripped by specious vertigos, they hold forth, prattle on, over-excite themselves. Haggard and idiotic, or logical and clairvoyant, they are always recognizable as possessed by that singular genius more variable than the myriad dragon: the Genius of Dynastic Decline. The more happily inspired, the strongest you shall see living out their last days and well-counted hours in feasting, with music, flowers, murders and wine; you shall see them dragging down with them into the abyss their friends, their favourites, mistresses bought at the price of a kingdom, their families, even their ancestors who are disinterred and dethroned with them.

There are not only resounding falls. Many had neither the honour nor the talent to perish with beauty. Death under the blade is rare; some were obliged to drink poison; some preferred the total intoxication of ideas, sanctity, no less fatal. Others escape and end up who knows where. Others do not end at all, and those are the only true guilty ones . . . But each of them, by a quirk, has stamped history, and all have accomplished up to the end in its time the holocaust – in its right time, I tell you, and have prepared the new beginning. May they merit a devotion, human jealousy! What they have done, is it not meritorious, inversely virtuous, more difficult perhaps then the daily practice of all the virtues?

Come. That this be a slow stroll through the dynastic Palaces: four thousand years of one continuous reign in operation! Come. Here is the end of the first era: exactly the painting which put the Sage and his disciples to flight!

It is the

QUAKING THRONE
OF THE HOUSE OF HSIA.

At the bottom, an enormous confusion; a storm swamp-like with colours and shapes one might qualify as animal; it is an assembly of three thousand men, flat on the ground.

At the top, The Unique – whose face is invisible since he is too far away in time: the seventeenth and last of the first family: the first of those who fall. By the curve of his shoulders and arms and by the delineation of his muscles, it is clear that he is very strong and tough, and that his sinews as they twang make the harsh sound of a bull's tendons, and that his hands which can twist bronze rip apart living buffaloes and tigers. Those are the virtues he incarnates, despising the virtue others venerate.

But he is depicted here not so much ready for the hunt or murder as for the rut; and his arms, with that movement, neither strangle nor smother anything but the delicate girl he loves, Mei-hsi of the infrequent smile on her violet mouth. The powerful kiss emprisons a fragile breast which throbs and blushes with pleasure, and from which could easily spurt – not acidulous mothers' milk – but the blood of noble mistresses.

One and the other delay the timeless movement in order to contemplate a little longer . . . that which you too see, now, disengaged from the primitive tumult: a spectacle organized as a great feast: they are enthroned on top of a pile of heaped-up meat, this reeking, edible pedestal.

It is a mountain on an island, since all around a river of wine flows and discharges into a circle. On the concave bank, three thousand men drink with their nose, their eyes and their mouths the composite flood which the Prince's liberality spreads out, and they estimate, from the other side of the river, the promises of the hillock of meats. This creates a gigantic homage girding the Son of the Sky and the elected companion. This creates three thousand vulgar, popular lusts, enlivening and celebrating better than nuptial words or orgiastic chants the imminent union, the consummation of the imperial act.

The mass drinks avidly, and wishes also to eat sincerely, since they have been famished and dying of thirst for nine days by sovereign order. A few, not very enthusiastic, sick or ungrateful subjects - are also obliged by posted marshals with whip lashes and spears, to lap, and to venerate the Prince as he so wills in the majesty of his desire.

*

It is impossible to conceal that, here and there, blotches in the confines of the sky, bad omens appear: a planet has left its path; there is that hirsute star; the face of the moon in double; and more troubling, more fatal than the prodigies and signs, in the shadow rises the virtuous visage of the founder of the second family . . .

This one will defeat and overthrow the other; history is there to witness. Is it not that which officially judges men? That is why history has discerned to this one, patron of the happy rebels, the honorable title Victor, and has cast on the other – the stronger one, the more male, that more of a man than all men – the posthumous sobriquet of 'Inhuman'.

FALL OF CHANG-YIN

Do not attempt here to see all at once. The eye of man cannot pierce with one glance the astonishing inventions of a woman; and the Painter, in order to omit nothing, has divided up the surface. This meticulous assemblage of small paintings depicts the games of the Ingenious, the girl of multiple delights. Others hone their fingers by twisting materials into garlands, in cosseting silk-worms in the tepid room... This one prefers to weave her life out of the chain of days and to clothe the body of her Imperial lover in that burning cloth. More than the antique Masters, she is here Teacher, Inspiration, Poet of the Fall of CHANG-YIN.

*

This then, like woman's work, is both unexpected and delicate. This has no other aim but to please and, vindicated in advance, can be looked on as one likes. Look:

A tower in the centre of the plain. A proud tower of jade with twenty pale jade doors, marbled green (the one called 'corpse's flesh'). Its tenfold foundations are raked backwards; uniting the pitiless, blue and dry Sky with the flat, livid land, transformed by ten years of drought. A symbol! But, come nearer: look more closely at these high clouds escaping from the throbbing walls – (like the Influx for all that which is translucent . . .) And even, *listen* to these high clouds, going discreetly from one direction to the other, from one world to another, from the spectacular to the sonorous: they are the sounds of nine hundred instruments placed by Her on each of the nine storeys and which have to play incessant unmorose choruses, untraditional, not old, so super-imposing their nine Skies: tunes of powdered dances, tunes of joy, tunes for nude dances, tunes for gambling, tunes for women's loving, tunes to drink wine, tunes reserved for men, tunes to stimulate the appetite, tunes to invite genies to sate themselves in debauch . . . The tenth storey, penetrated by all the musics, is the reserved lodge. May the Emperor stoop to rest here. May he clothe himself with this tower of feasts, impenetrable to guilt and virtue.

*

Elsewhere, look at this fire-red rectangle, cut in two by a shimmering bar. It is the Sea-of-Judgements, traversed by the Bridge-of-Bronze – that unique greased beam. The guilty dance across it; the innocent are perturbed, slip, fall into the fire: the innocent are separated from the guilty.

This woman has the spirit of Justice.

*

And the material spirit. Even though sterile, she had the idea of seeing with her own eyes how man is conceived and born: she has caused the painless deaths of gravid women in order to disembowel them at leisure. As for the warriors seen crossing the glacial ford in high morning – there they are, their shinbones cracked open so that she might know if they possess marrow redder and hotter than the others, or not.

*

And further, she wished to show the Emperor what happens in the savage liberty of the night. So she ordered out the Great Imperial Hunt, depicted by this long dark frieze crossed by running fires. So many of them that one would say a cavalry of stars, the beaters, torches in hand, drive the pallid game. They are no longer wild boars and sows, nor she-bears and bears, nor quadrupeds with horns, but human females and naked men, hair floating in the wind, long legs scissoring through the night in a panting stampede. All, male and female, have to pass in front of the hide; all, with a shot of an invisible bow, are pinned to the ground.

*

However, that prudent couple by itself refrains from touching the notched arrow, and clasp each other beneath strung death. It is because they know that they will be spared if they unite freely there, under the hide, before Him. – But, more thoroughly than by an arrow we sense them transfixed by a shot from pitiless eyes . . .

*

Here and there, a few wheezing old men: Sages, or those who pretended to be. For they have dared to censure the most lovely novelties painted here. The jade tower seemed to them too extravagant; the music sacrilege; the fiery judgements equivocal; the driven hunt shameless! So, following the popular saying that a Sage '*always has seven orifices in his heart*', the censured 'Ingenious' has determined to find out if these old men were sages, or not, and their reproaches justified or not. She has counted on her fingers the natural holes in their hearts.

This woman has the spirit of logic.

*

This secret corner of the painting, effected by too much ogling no doubt, is obscure to divulge, except for its epigraph which reads: 'The Ingenious organizes an offering to the Emperor of a group of young girls she trained by hand, and, unseen, oversees the first audience.'

This woman has the spirit of conjugality.

*

*   *

And yet, you are disappointed. She, the Inspiration, is absent from all these paintings . . . Like you, I look for the cunning Princess, Mediator between dynastic fall and Him, condemned, who is not seen either; Him for whom all the spectacles were organized. History merely recounts that He was intelligent and used his wit to confound his critics, but gives us no detail of his appearance.

As for Her, perhaps it is better she were never painted; and furthermore, let us decline to describe her ourselves – from too great a despair lest we fall under her spell on the spot; or, even worse, lest the Incomparable, seen all of a sudden in her nudity, shows herself to be similar and alike to all her fellow women.

HUMILIATION OF TCHEOU

Only two figures, but in human scale. That one who stands upright, covered in plate-armour and helmeted – he has the red muzzle and that conquering eye of a battle veteran. The army insignia on his chest show him to be a marshal of a powerful feudal clan, Ts'in, who for three hundred years, have gobbled up kingdoms one by one, '*like silk-worms chew the leaves of the mulberry tree*'.

And this name of Ts'in can no longer be read on any battlefield.

*

But one cannot make out either the insignia or the rank or the identity of the other figure, who, turning his back to us, humiliates himself at the ankle level of the puffed-up warrior. This prostrate creature allows only the lower parts of his robe and the soles curved in the Palace fashion to be seen. And no one would dare to say who is there, if the image and this truly historic posture did not have their fitting place among the declines and falls. Whether one likes it or not, this ridiculous portrait of an Emperor is recognizable, the last of the TCHEOU. By means of this posture he offers in exchange for his shameful life – 'He offers,' as the chronicle says, 'the thirty thousand towns still loyal to him, the three hundred thousand heads (different from his own) still on living shoulders. If it is accepted, he will vanish without delay; He even promises to die . . . in the forthcoming year, if that is what is wanted; earlier if that is advantageous. But not too quickly, above all not today, not on this day which he inundates with his wailings . . .'

*

The brave soldier, happy and satisfied, considers it agreeable to look down on an Emperor, for one unique time, from the height of an erect man. – You are surprised they dared to paint so ignominiously the abasement of a Son of Heaven. Nameless posture! and yet, if worthy irony, rather than the rationalism of literati, made up historical epithets, it is truly to this prostrate creature and not to others that, better than a mask, the posthumous title of 'The Rump' should be applied.

*

And that is how well-governed houses end! That is how families fall and clans perish! This exemplary lineage of the TCHEOU! Eight hundred years of hereditary virtues . . . Thirty-four Sovereigns . . . promises, omens, prodigies! The purest resolutions; circulars, decrees rained, as it were, out of the Sky! The paid counsels of the Sage and Saint of the country of Lou, Confucius, the precise witness of that grandeur tumbling towards its fall – there it is! all ends in shipwreck, dying at the feet of an uncivilized lout, astounded by his easy victory.

In this end without pride, in this wreck without beauty, you could search in vain for his accomplice, the woman.

At least decency has prevailed here; there is no woman here.

TOMB OF TS'IN

Three superimposed hills; three hills backing up to the unique summit, nobly convex under the hollow Sky; and on the right, and from the left, the long descent of the reverse slope vanishing into horizontal infinity.

Despite the amplitude of the base, despite the attitude of setting up its volume and its fronton in defiance of the rains of the atmosphere and of the blows of the earth, this is not a natural sport of the land, but the monument of eight hundred thousand man–days, erected to the glory of the Only, King of TS'IN, Emperor ONE.

*

*   *

Indeed! you could look for ten thousand years more

and nothing would change in this painting; merely the red-gold tone baked by time – and nothing more would appear . . .

But even so the anxiety you betray as you look . . . suspecting there you know not what of immense . . . But this contrast between the erstwhile human masses and the absence of all men here . . . But this discord, this reversed challenge between the expected object: 'DECLINE OF TS'IN' and this grandiose structured edifice . . .

But no! You will see nothing if you remain thus, stunned spectators overwhelmed by appearances. Let me guide you deep inside. You must penetrate this tomb. For that, shut your round eyes, your visible eyes, and accept to see blindly each word I say.

*

* *

. . . The surface is breached. Here we are on the *other* side of the earth, but not in blackness: we are following the Path of the Soul into the heart of the monument. It is a long, vaulted corridor, lit only at the far end, at five hundred paces' distance, by yellow fires whose oblique reflections encrusted in the walls, caught by the countless figurative scenes on the side walls, rebound at us. – All is covered with storied bricks. Touch them. Feel how brick is akin to earth, and, for a tomb, more intimate, do you not agree, for its decoration? They trail off, out of sight, three thousand diminutive personages as tall as your hand, delineated in hard semi-relief. Each next to its fellow without overlapping or concealment, they are disposed over three levels.

As high as a hand! And yet, each of their gestures has shaken the Empire and echoed as far as the barbarian Marches. It is He alone who is present here. His mighty deeds throw space into relief: Look then! Blind men or vampires would delight in groping over all of it: It is the extraordinary birth, the conquests, the triumph of the House of TS'IN; it is over there that the Empire is transformed into a seamless basin and kingdoms are stirred and kneaded into one single loaf. Each scene is simple and clear.

Here, the young king, his majority scarcely attained, declares that all who oppose his acts shall first be decapitated and then boiled; then listened to . . . perhaps.

Here the cauldron sings, the executioner's block on which heads are laid is ready. But the young king himself takes the censor by the hand, raises him up and makes him Chief Councillor.

Here, you contemplate him, lashing stones which bleed and having painted blood-red a rock which refuses to blush.

Here, out of respect for his revered mother – even though unworthy – he slaughters in Han-tan all the old people who saw his birth and claimed he was a bastard.

Here, he frustrates a hired assassin's dagger. Here and there, in passing, you have seen how he destroys enemy kingdoms. He only spares his own.

Here, he decides to abolish the past behind him. He makes a bonfire of all books; he buries alive the Readers of all the books. He refuses all precursors, the good ones and the others.

And he proclaims himself Origin, Emperor ONE.

*

Master of all known lands under the Sky, rabid master of the living, he claims to tame even death and demands from his furnaces the potion of the Drug, drinkable Gold, the Wine of Joy which makes Immortals. To win the battle for the recipe, he sends a fleet, an entire people out to sea. Here is the departure towards the Islands-in-the-Sea of three thousand male virgins and three thousand girls with pure bellies, demanded by the divine alchemists . . . (You shall not see the return journey.)

Here, he grows impatient, and, as the Drug is long in coming, the Panacea is mixed for him, more efficient, out of cinnabar and sublimated time – which fully distills the body, dispensing ubiquity, spiritual life, Being in fact.

He deigns to accept the cup: here He drinks . . .

*

*   *

And here we are before the sepulchre, having entered the vault shining with yellow lamps, having left behind the obsessional corridor over-full with images, for this perfect hollow cube, solid on its pavement of bronze cast in one slab.

By magic! that mass of women is still there! those two hundred concubines buried alive with Him, and whom yellow night perpetuates, without awakening and without agony . . . But high up, it is more astounding: this ceiling which supports the weight of three hills, seems to be woven out of the thinnest drawings of the Sky. Below, you walk on depictions of the earth, rivers and seas. All around are the models of the Palaces of the destroyed kingdoms which he brought back amid his own; there are jewels, rare objects, worlds he imagined or which his desire conjured up . . .

But already you listen no longer; you lean over the sarcophagus; you attempt to see inside, through the crack between the top and the sides . . . Yes, you can see inside: it is empty.

*

*   *

Men will tell you, '*five years after his death and the Rites, the great Tomb was ransacked by the rebellious hordes, the corpse flayed, the jewels melted down*' . . . and that we are not the first to penetrate up to here. Historians' tales. The tomb is empty, that is true, but the whole Empire is still filled by Him, administered by His law, united into one whole by His strength.

And as for Him, he is neither here nor there. He did not stoop to rest long in his sepulchre, that is it. He has disproved the poet: he has not '*known the sadness of whitened bones*'. Perhaps the Potion was the right one and He is not dead. Such is his living grandeur that this name: CHE HOUANG-TI raises and rends the earth. Back away, let us leave the tomb in haste.

Here He is, as He was, coming towards us: alone without decorations or attributes, spilling over into the space around Him, the stocky majestic man with a prominent nose, wide eyes, the chest swelling like the breast of a bird of prey under his cuirass. Him, and nothing else around. Both hands hard against his belly, he controls with difficulty more of a belly-full of pride than that of the rest of mankind. There is the man who tames men, or, at his ease, devours them.

He stands erect legs akimbo.

ABDICATION OF THE WESTERN HAN

Can you see anything more here than two friends, two united brothers? They hold each other by the hand. The one on the left – ugly face, thin and aflame – is dressed in common fabrics; but he watches over the other with his ardent stare, more beautiful than a daughter of joy, whose neck is noble and plump, the brow curved like that of a grasshopper, the eyebrow lunar and the eye long; and who wears on his finery designs of the most important colour: black. It is T'ong-hsien, the favourite, rich with promise. Hardly smiling, he listens to his friend, leaning on him and who tenderly suggests:

'Would you, oh! would you like me to do what Yao did for Chouen! Would you accept? Accept . . .'

*

. . . What Yao did for Chouen: he abdicated. It is the true meaning of this historical painting. For he who speaks and begs, offers nothing less than the throne. He can offer it. He holds it: he is the Emperor. What more noble thing from one friend to another: to give all to him whom you prefer above all!

*

But what provoked the censores' recriminations? Was it simply for professional reasons? For virtue's sake? Out of spleen? It is true that the handsome favourite neglects the public functions of his office which he delegates to underlings . . . It is all the better to fulfil roles which cannot be delegated. It is true that already he has his tomb next to the imperial tumulus . . . Thus he shows that he will rejoin in death his imperial lover. He alone in the Palace does not desert him at night: better than the frivolous Empress, he already shares all the anxieties of the days of the Throne and the anguished dreams of He who is menaced by the Sky.

*

Could it be such a great friendship that the censors denounced? Could it be so much friendship soon will bring about the fall of the dynasty! For already, on closer inspection, the quadruple look turns troubled:

visible and increasing, the usurper Wang-Mang, robber of the seal, iniquitous sabre slashing in two the dynasty like a man through his waist, creates panic in the four pupils of their eyes.

*

* *

And if any one of you is curious about the corresponding period in the barbarian chronicles, he should know that, during the infamous reign of Wang-Mang, is born in the West that Sage whom the Romans have since made their genie and unique protector, Jesus. And it is in his name, from now on, that these non-tributary races calculate universal time. (Which obliges them sometimes to count backwards; to claim that the first dynasty, the ancestral house of HSIA, goes back 'two thousand two hundred and five years before their era!')

Thus they posit a neutral moment in the middle of continuous time . . .

FUNERAL GALLOP OF THE EASTERN HAN

Out of contempt, the image of Hsien-ti, the last of the late Han, has not been preserved; doubtless because the painter refused to freeze so much flabby daily goodwill, and a static dull end.

This section of the dynastic procession would be empty but for the rich generosity of the funerary workers. In place of a Palace vanished without a sound, we have there some bas-reliefs – or rather rubbings of them – those thin stamped rice papers, those vital shades, sharp, shining black on a completely white ground.

No consistency, no reflection, no suppleness, but energy – in that apparent dispersion – unique in being able to move, quiver, depart in all directions: not one of those beings, whom one could have imagined petrified some eighteen hundred years ago, stands still or emits an image of its death . . . These infantry men, look at them, from left to right, racing off with long diagonal strides. They escort, or judging from their enthusiasm one might say they push the two-wheeled wagons with their parasols, drawn by snorting, rearing, sleek, rounded horses bursting with muscles! Next to them, tegulate riders thunder along on their sixty-four hoofs. Chase has been given by the entire calvacade, from left to right, its coursers, its falcons, its huntsmen, and its dove-catchers, and fur and feather which will be taken in nets, in beaks, in jaws. They are off to war: archers, on foot or mounted, shoot in front and to the rear. The very animals chase after each other: those which can be captured, broken-in, or slain: the camel with its soft pads and dragon's neck, the elephant with its trunk, and the cuirassed Western cow with its horned nose! Others even more rare: the Unicorn led on a leash by this thin bent figure who sways as he walks, sleeves and elbows sticking out; and the stag born out of the winged horse which the bizarre woman with the full face, supple body and bare breasts is riding. Without slowing the pace, here comes the solar three-legged bird, and the lunar hare, very busy under its ears, with its mortar in its arms where it crushes and grinds the drug of long life – decidedly too late for all the defunct. Jugglers and acrobats keep tumbling from the high clouds amid those on foot. Heads upside down, they do cartwheels and spring up again.

Monkeys, with or without tails, chase each other. Faster than them all, the large wagons with spoked wheels, drawn by those famous trotters – long necks and splayed noses, the tribute of Soghdiana . . .

Thus, in the hollows of small chambers, on the capitals of funerary columns, around the booming terracotta coffin, there is a mad rush of fantastic phantoms fleeing from who knows what, *en route* for who knows where. If the erosion of outside rains or the intimate casting and the exhalations of flesh have somewhat eaten into the original contours, at least there remains these harsh drawings, half-skeletal and half-human, these fish bones on which the implacable rubbing seizes. Birds fly, quadrupeds pace, men run; wagons tumble into water where fish swim; boats descend rivers. Several unmounted frenzied horses fight their way back through the others . . . so many, you say, that it is impossible to focus on any single one? So, follow only this rider:

This Thin Man, on the back of a unicorn which has lost three of its legs – the remaining one tensed over the space in front. The jolting stride more unmanageable than the bucking of a young nomad stallion, but the Uplifted raises his steed with a beat of its membraned wings. The arid thighs and tibias have a more powerful grip than than the muscled fetlocks; the large foot drums against the rear flank; the widespread and free fetlocks continue to disdain the stirrup. It is he who looses and urges on his steed, and he goes in an indrawn breath like that of the huge ambiguous flowers – green poppies? – bent aside by his passing, tossing their voluted stalks in his pursuit.

*

Was it a living man, a vampire, or an allusion in movement? There is no name over him, no more than over his thousands of brothers fixed to the slabs which they pull, to the granite and sandstone which they support.

In place of a extinguished Emperor, here are the people and the army of an era precipitated in one bound towards its fall: the entire cavalry dynasty charges – at a walk, at a trot or at a gallop – towards the abyss.

If not, what other exegesis could explain the ardent ride of the Thin Man, and those flowers curled over the hindquarters on top of him?

RIDICULOUS FEAST OF CHOU-HAN

This painting is made for laughter – at its loudest when friends dine together, when belts, towards the tenth course, are loosened; when mouths politely belch in appreciation of the quality of the food. It is at precisely this moment that it is fitting to look at this one: a banquet of friends, the reciprocal invitation of three princes: tables, cups, bowls, soup tureens full of juice; smoked delicacies, sauces into which fingers dip and taste; when appetities marinate and eyes sail on before the most delicate stomachs are sated. It is a fine feast well served.

Each at his place, the three kings, peers in title, all Emperors of their own free will – and so near their triple fall, look at each other not without laughing. Their clothing and their hats guffaw as they do. The guests, the Ministers and the servants and the doorman and those small boys under the tables – the tables as well, the columns and the ceiling – share in this laughter, whose butt is one of the three – who laughs louder than the others.

*

They hail him: 'Hey, there! Sovereign of the land of Chou, show us your fine manners!'

The other salutes them and waddles like a well-trained duck. Everybody laughs, he as well. Someone adds:

'Don't they know how to dance in your country?'

As a reply, here he is dancing. And the hilarity is redoubled. And in order to complete the laughter, to die of it right there, under the tables, he is goaded even further:

'You don't regret that crazy wild land of Chou?'

He continues to make excuses, to thank them for their interest in his tastes – which causes further paroxysms – when faithful Kiao-Tch'eng, the only one not to laugh but to chew on his tongue at the outrage, jumps to his feet and leaps before the ridiculous Master, and replies for him:

'The tombs of Our Ancestors lie there, in the holy land of Chou. How could we forget their manners?'

His aspect is so awful that the pent-up laughter is swallowed back. The noble words, better than any rapier, cram it back down their throats.

MORBID ECSTASY OF TSIN

No playing, no movement here. No murders, no blood no wounds no stains (at least apparent ones). No debauchery even virtuous through excess in its abomination; and yet, here it is that which was as disastrous for Tsin as much as the preceding spectacles were for the others.

*

That Emperor, just recognizable under the rough monkish robe of Buddha, is simply sitting before a writing-desk. The slow eyes fixed on us do not halt at our eyes, but project their troubling serenity towards the space-behind. Only one gesture, and that unmoving: one of the raised right hand holding the brush point downwards.

Everything is suspended on that point. For, with a stroke, the brush and the fingers, promulgating the Decision, can hurl into combat the hundred thousand well-armed soldiers whose percussive vigour would win the imminent battle. But neither the fingers nor the brush descend: – how could you ignore the fact that the clamour of armies, the tumult of victory; all the rumblings of the world, finally, dissolve in a quiver which dies away . . .

*

Could he not at least spare or avenge his sons who are being killed? For he hears, as we do, not far off from here, the throat-slitting and the death rattles.

The brush is not lowered, does not tremble: – you know well how love, even paternal love, is a constraint, and that descendants only prolong the ignorance and pain of living . . .

*

He prefers then, abandoning the use of force and his sons, to buy back the women they violate not far from here? – No. Woman is above all a burden, the arresting, the obstacle to Great Deliverance.

*

Let him choose a decent death by poison . . . But he refuses that somewhat indiscreet taste – since life and death are the twin reflections of the same shadow . . .

He remains as he is, hand raised, this brush – whose stroke would change the Underbelly of the whole Sky – suspended.

*

*   *

No need for haste; except for us the press of rebels outside. Nothing exists; except for him the Knowledge that nothing exists which he possesses. Nothing out of the depths of that esctatic soul obliges the accomplishment of the gesture, nor the eyes to shut or blink: on the contrary, here they are growing and encompassing the space . . .

(Come. Let us not tarry before them, or you will see the Painting vanish like a bubble sneezing its colours and you will feel in your soul the fainting away of those hot passions of all the colours which constitute its human worth. Much more than debauchery and madness, this is communicable, absorbing, exhausting . . .)

To end it all, they smother him with blankets.

TITUBATION OF TSI

This can only be seen when drunk; it is full of dancing fumes through which staggers a Minister of the Rites! Useless, and even incongruous, to keep one's composure here. Just as the Painter preparing himself to throw this on with one splash of paint; just as this good King Kao-Yang did night and day before drying the last of his cups – you must drink. Swallow then with small sips the smoking wine over here.

*

Oh! there is no important elaborately constructed scenery! And first of all, what difference can it make to you that these folk are made out of paint or of meat, that they dance ten leagues away from my eye or inside it? I see them. Hence I grant them provisionally and consubstantially existence. They take advantage of it to frolic about shamelessly. They do not possess our dignity. They are not drunk enough. But, we, let us not go in for Allegorical Painting. You should understand: these people are not concepts! The painter has quite simply formalized in colour and glue the maelstrom of hypothetical reflections. I grasp it. I surprise myself in fact. Undertand what I express with too much volubility perhaps for still fasting spirits.

And him, there he is, the good old drinker Kao-Yang, how he must love me! unless he too is . . . Very intelligent! Discoveries, lapidary inventions: the steles are there to bear witness. It is him, it is really him, down on all fours. (But one is more stable like that than on two feet.) He still cherishes the idea of marrying off his mother to a Turk – nuptial bed included. It is a strange idea. He realizes afterwards that the rite is not provided for in the Ceremonies. And he sobs, flat on his stomach at the feet of the terrified Dowager from whom he demands in expiation eighty-one strokes on the buttocks. (His own.)

Morality is preserved since the Sky has nine levels, and nine times nine . . . You have understood at last! History tells this story exactly the wrong way round.

He was such an excellent man! Just look at this proof of excellence, of which you would be incapable: an excellence, to make the entire sea weep over the entire Sky. There: He treats his generals well; He seats them on his throne, one on top of the other, and He quenches their thirst from his magic cup, always full. He begs the pretty lady Joy-of-Dawn to quench their other desires by giving herself there, on the spot, as a gift from Him. And as the lady hesitates, he undresses her and offers her with his own hands. This scene emits a haze of excellence.

And this other, a certain impression of Truth. Monks and philosophers fight over it. They are there, disciples of Buddha or of Tao, who all claim Uniqueness. But the Prince is an incomparable judge. He orders that once and for all each argument be spread out in front of him. Not in order and one after the other, which weakens them and can be qualified as 'incomprehensible'; but in one bunch, one splurge, – he even says: 'In one pile!' and assumes the responsibility of discerning the true Truth, and to listen against the background of uproar.

*

Then, all together, Tao-che naming the Unnameable, and Shaven-Pates causing the Causes to cascade and the wheel of the Law to turn, all the Doctors of peace fight amongst themselves, all the Motionless Ones fling themselves about before the Judge, finally drunk by slightly too strong ideas, and judiciously asleep.

DEIFICATION OF PEI-TCHEOU

It is more – or less – a man you see, riding his favourite beast. Under the appearances of this benevolent Genie astride the traditional peacock is a mad king, deified by himself. The painting is red-brown, old-red and black, smoked by incense and lamp-black, buttered by the devotional oil of hands, like those big pious frescoes which dwell in temples, and which penetrate the walls with their greasy touch.

*

Symmetrical to his glory, King Yu of the Cheou shows himself: raising the right hand, lowering the other, he releases the everlasting gesture of all the Genies saviours of all the worlds, and which thus designate the Skies they precede from and the earth which they water with compassion.

No other image is permitted. The background on both sides could be accessible to the living perhaps... But it has been impregnated, out of respect, with a dark varnish. He alone – god – wishes to be seen; and from his chin to his nether regions he unspreads on the stellate robe the name of the hypostases which He attributes to himself and the Entities he encompasses. But whosoever appears before him and dares to contemplate the divine must prepare himself by three nights of abstinence, followed by an entire day of ablutions. –

Have you done so?

*

Then, content yourselves with respectfully raising your eyes to his mount. The god-carrying bird, this male peacock, is set frontally like Him. The tail forms an aureole. The feet two worthy columns. The head with its small grey eyes precisely hides his navel.

STAGE IN THE FALL OF SOUEI

It is a city in the evening: a strong and powerful crenellated city of which we are both the guests and the masters – for, maintained by geomancy at the crossing of the two cardinal paths, we have in front of us the horizon of the South. Here we are higher than all the buildings, except that which carries us on high, the Pavilion of the drum-bearing Tower. Rather than the flattened faces of the façades, it is the waving roofs that we dominate. They jostle and push each other, wings outstretched, those mighty birds brooding over human families. You can see all the ridges, the horns and the flying chevrons; they fight among themselves for the dentellated diagram of the Sky; they call for the penetration of high clarity into obscure corrosion: all the Divination of the City. And it is evening.

Further off than the roofs, the battlements. And further off than the battlements, the fly-buzzing tradesmen's suburbs. And over it, the mountain line cut by a breach: the two promontories affront each other without one of them ever seizing the other by the muzzle, owing to the shining stream of the river between them.

But turn to the right: here is the West. This painting, unlike the others, is not arranged in one dimension. Here is well and truly yesterday's horizon and the set sun and the final shots it continues to fire at the atmosphere.

And turn also towards the North, facing the land of cold: those are wrinkled hills mounting each other right in the middle of a yellow land, entirely peopled by sepulchres. It is a funeral pillow under the head of the City, weighing down with its nape and its sleep on the Ancestors buried there. For now the totality of night falls on them and on their offspring. Darkness settles, exalting the whiteness, drowning the blackness. Indeed it is black in the North, and it would be futile for you to try and extend over there a little more daytime.

Turn then towards the gate which shall be tomorrow – towards the East where the moon rises in a lake more pearly than the days. Distances seem shorter when light descends down to street level, on the forecourts of Palaces, Ministries and Halls of Judgement, and, lower down, in the blind alleys where the unofficial rate for delights and temporal joys is haggled over. You witness the comings and goings, barter, gifts. A busy life, a nocturnal commerce takes place here while the other cantons go to sleep.

And turn for the last time: here we are again facing South, astounded by the full circle of movement: this painting with its four angles is therefore endless and circular like the horizon itself? Yes. And the city we inhabit thus is no other but Lo-Yang once again the Capital through the grace of the second and last of the SOUEI, of Yang-Ti?

You agree it is really that? The breach to the South is the '*Mountain-gate of the Dragon*', Longmen. The twin mortuary hill to the North is Mang-chan. The red fires of the western sky, and the earthly eastern incandescence – ourselves, between yesterday and tomorrow, fixed in the middle of the tower – and these five cardinal points in accordance with the most local expertise; it is truly at Lo-Yang that we are . . .

*

*   *

No. A thousand leagues further to the North, in the middle of the desert, surrounded by flat expanses like seas without walls and without buildings, on the grassy high plateaux where never a Capital City nor a Chinese city have established their logical grid plans.

This smothering and endless painting is the resting tent which Yang-Ti, on his journey to the outposts, demanded set up about Him, every evening on the four sides of space. As soon as a halt was called, even in the heart of the deserts of sand, he exacted that in one thrust, painters and soldiers erect over a circle of two thousand paces this silk two thousand paces long. He deems it fitting for Him that the Emperor never roams as a nomad, and never reaches nor lives under a crude sky nor on an unsurveyed plot. Condescending to move about in the unknown, he does not permit a change of scenery. That the entire city of the day be present at the crepuscular audience, at the night watch, this prescribed by ceremonial.

That was not understood in his time. Yang-Ti left behind the reputation of an egoist and a sedentary, since, true to Himself, he disliked to contemplate the world in any other way but at its centre.

ANCESTRAL PORTRAIT

An ancient and noble Dame, seated exactly in front of us, the two long equal eyes a little sunken by the years; the brow smooth, the mouth drawn in a single line; the chin small and round, the cheekbones angular; the hair coloured black-as-hair elaborately festooned.

And directly in front of us – like the face, the pleats of her robe, the wide drooping sleeves – is the throne addorsed against a great halo of gold which forms the fullest of moons.

It is an ancestral portrait. The painter here, executing royal orders, has pierced the two eyes of that bottomless well of the pupils – for you could have, by means of that well, attained the soul of the portrait. But what need? That symmetry, those concordances: fingers interlaced in agelong serenity; solid knees and above all that face seen frontally, as well balanced as a monument; those flat colours on the impassive side-wall, and the perfect circle describing its everlasting contour . . .

Is it not the very presence of the Goddess of Considered Compassion? Nothing else dwells on that brow? Those nostrils are full of perfumes. That mouth will only give birth to tender words. And those feet have trodden the middle way.

According to her dynastic rank, it is the image of the Dowager Empress Wou, of the T'ANG. And the painter has taken pains to inscribe in elegant letters the emblems, the attributes, the honorific names and the titles which her merit procured for her and which she deigned to accept: '*High Guardian of the Tchakra*' (that golden disc propagator of the Law), '*Light illuminating nothingness*' (a symbol employed here for the first time just as the character '*Sun and Moon united over the void* ' which depicts it here).

Finally the prophecy of Maïtreya which she incarnated in her woman's body by a special marvel: '*Before becoming Buddha, you shall be reborn one more time in a woman's body . . .*' And these three gentle words: '*Holy supernatural Mother*'.

*

And you are taken aback to see here such an image

of celestial majesty . . . such a mirror of the purest goodness . . .

*

But the enumeration of her virtues does not come to a halt so soon. Here, there is not all that could be said: the Annals make the following commentary:

'*Concubine of the father, defrocked nun, Imperial spouse of the son, first in the line of succession, murderess of her daughter in her cradle so as to accuse her rival of the deed; murderess of her over-intelligent son; murderess of the other Empress whom she shortened by lopping off the feet and arms and preserved in a jar full of wine; shameless mistress of an abbot of two hundred young monks; slayer of her Emperor-husband whose head swelled to bursting by witchcraft; sacrilegious by making a female sacrifice to the Sky through the investiture of the mountain, she revolted the good earth of the Empire which vomited itself up in boils of mud. However she received the impossible honours of an eclipse of the male Sun! She had corrupted the very principles of Yin and Yang, the deepest foundations of the Universe . . .*'

We bow down before you, '*Holy supernatural Mother*'.

IMPOTENCE OF T'ANG

These wishy-washy colours and quavering lines... The authentic gestures of the sovereign have not permitted a more lively or precise rendering – nor his eyes, a little tired. The painter first proposed to illustrate the '*Noble imperial tortures*'. But Wen-tsong immediately made modifications. Like that all the time! There then are personages full of hesitations about what they should have done in history.

Nevertheless it was well deserved the death of this Minister Wang-Ya, persecutor of the eunuchs: he is sawn in two, in the middle of the market, at the foot of a pole – quickly, and without futile agonies, since the Emperor had not ordained that he suffer for a long time. Lower down, the family gathers up the pieces and buries them: since the Emperor had not said that they be deprived of burial. Further on: the eunuchs open up the grave and hurl the bones into the river:

since the Emperor had issued no edict about a funeral.

Follow now these emissaries: they hunt down very young children, kidnapping or buying them, and carry them off. They will be fed on a diet rich in meat and fats, so as to extract for the Emperor fine livers full of blood and rapid hearts full of strong air out of which his medicine will be made. – But, very close by, there are the emissaries disavowed: had the Emperor ever desired such medicine? He denies it and condemns his minions. It is their own spleens and biles which become indispensable to embalm his remorse.

Now he plays at the Conqueror-despoiler of cities! So he has stripped and bound, as if offered up to him, ten young girls guaranteed virgins. They lie down, forcibly separating their thin arms and round thighs. The powerful victor receives them and turns away after a glance: He had never seen girls thus naked. As they weep and wail, he quickly has them unbound and dressed; caresses them lightly and sends them away laden with cakes and pearls.

Then, the official painter suggests painting him still living among the Great Succession of the Good and the Sages. And the Emperor draws himself up, rolls his eyeballs, grinds his teeth:

'To whom pray do you imagine Our face resembles?'

'To the holy faces of Yao and Chouen . . .' replies the other politely.

The Emperor says: 'Sacrilege!'

He orders that they heat up the cauldron for flattterers . . . then changes his mind and orders that he be painted at once as a handsome tyrant. He skims through the annals, forcing himself to ape the most famous infamous postures . . . But, bursting into tears of rage, he well knows he can never assume them.

*

(All this composed of crossings-out, hesitances of the brush.)

LOGICAL MASTERY OF SONG

The scene is more than expressive and overflows with useful knowledge: the Emperor, half reclining on his day-bed, displays a serious mouth, an eyebrow heavy with philosophical thoughts. He admonishes the Crown Prince standing, out of deference, a few steps away.

But the daily lesson goes further than a father's education of a son. On both sides, gathering in the twin streams of the cloak of words, see the Great civil Protector and the General of the Army. As the child learns, so do the Ministers and, via them, the entire population.

*

The Emperor expounds:

'That the Universe, and all the beings it contains, issue from two Principles, coeternal, infinite, distinguishable, but inseparable, NORM and MATTER.

'That there is not, between these two Principles, antecedence or posteriority of origin, but of Reason – and a dignity. (The Norm not falling under the senses, Matter supporting them.)

'That one and the other, without soul or contour, are individualized in the flesh out of which each of us is formed, and which, for a time, limits a segment of Norm, which, at its hour, returns to the infinite when the finite in the flesh dissolves, decomposes.'

The Emperor considers:

'If one should deny primordial Nothingness – and sure of the eternity of Norm and Matter, discern to the latter such an appellation as: '*Great Rarefaction*', or perhaps '*Great Harmony*', so as to confer on the union of the one to the other that supreme rank: '*Great Unity*', '*Great Beginning*', '*Great Mutation*', '*Great Realized Being*'.

The Emperor deigns to comment:

'Norm and Matter have existed since the beginning of time. Each being therefore is made of Norm and Matter. Norm was not prior to Matter. Norm more noble than Matter, cannot exist without it; and even though unique, categorizes itself in diversity. Eternal Norm is incarnate in the ephemeral. Norm and Matter were before Heaven and Earth were. Heaven and Earth are Norm and Matter. Norm and Matter are other than Heaven and Earth.'

And the Emperor finally decides:

'That the World is truly a maelstrom, insubstantial in its central matrix - more and more dense and compact and formal at its periphery; made concrete like the shell around the soft egg.'

From now on,

'That it should no longer be taught, because of an absurd misapprehension, that the nine spheres in the heavens curl around each other as the concentric rings of the onion - but truly that they compose, unrolling from the centre to the outside and in all dimensions at one and the same time, the Nine Volutes enspiralled by the maelstrom of the Universe - and there is no radius.'

And it is thus that, neglecting festive aromas, smiling from a distance on the congress of men and women, the Emperor gets drunk on his thoughts alone, and delights in the pure embrace of his concepts: soaked, better than any Army General, in the thirty-two principles of Warfare, he deploys them in defence or attack of his Palaces of Logic alone.

He will resolve the problem of knowing if Reason comes before feelings, or the latter before Reason. He will determine if the Great Void at the end of the world is solid in function of its speed or of its definition.

*

The civil Minister, well brought up, admits defeat, beaten by the logomachia of the Master who has just complimented him on his intelligent zeal. The Warrior, somewhat apart, trembles in all his heavy limbs. More violently than siege-catapults, the Words strike strong enough to smash his face in.

He dares not approve too loudly. Above all he dares not contradict. But, while the Philosospher leads his well-organized troops into combat, the Military Man, anxious despite himself, recalls that the Northern Hordes already occupy the cold provinces; that they are more than a million down there, menacing and mobile. He knows that for two hundred years the Dynasty retreats and disengages towards the South, abandoning the cities, the canals, the rivers and the fields whose diagonal furrows, ploughed to halt old-fashioned chariots, have been unable to slow down the advancing gallop of Mongol strides . . .

And that soon they will end up with the rawest savages!

*

But such is the virtue of logic and the imposing majesty of Words, that the veteran reins in his disquiet, listens more carefully, pretends to understand and always stays silent.

FINAL GAMES OF YUAN

No. This painting is not done in the dark and ferocious colour of Mongol standards – which you know already. Nothing here is reminiscent of their favourite subject – which you await already: the stocky bearded horseman, with flashing eyes below his fur cap, trotting rapidly and returning gaily from the hunt... It is thus that the hordes pirouetted down from the Heavenly-Hills to the Land-of-Grass...

It has nothing to do with them. But here is the exact, scrupulous image of the last days of the Khan of the Strong! Here is the apotheosis cooked up by the runt of the Great Nomad Ancestor: this grandson is above all a musician and a technician.

Admire his proudest invention: the magical Clepsydra; haunted from dawn onwards by genie-dolls who arrive to mark the hour by beating bells and cymbals. At night, there are plaster ghosts who direct the ringing. When one of the twelve hours empties, lions appear, which he himself has modelled using the most ferocious images out of printed books. – At midday, Immortals made out of painted cardboard take off and fly into fake grottoes. They come down again at midnight.

You can well believe that to manipulate these very small clock movements is more delicate than ruling over an Empire which feeds itself and populates itself – despite taxes and wars.

But learn also that to animate these dolls is nothing compared to the complicated machinery of the living Dancing Girls: The power of a man is astounding who is capable of organizing, step by step and movement after movement, the harmony of a hundred and twenty women's bodies simultaneously!

*

Of all History's spectacles, this one is the most instructive . . . It was at least the boast of its director, Son of Heaven and Grand Master of battles. – He would have been surprised if it were pointed out to him how many of elegant dynastic declines themselves contain their decadence in their fall; – and that with him we fall very low indeed.

LIBERATION OF MING

Not one man, not a living creature here except this gigantic tree, which fills the entire painted surface.

Solitary, its fine head of hair and one hundred arms create a concave forest under the encompassing sky, it absorbs the light and one sees nothing in the enclosure it covers but the patinated blood-brown of its trunk: dark green and blood-brown, no other colour. The bark is entirely spiralled as if from year to year it twisted itself to escape from some hold or other or to obey the sun. Its uprooted roots clasp hard the soil they lift up. The leaves are countless painted one by one. Do you already know of a case with the landscape dedicated to one tree, without mountains over it, without running water under it, nor that infinitesimal traveller, right at the bottom, who cranes his head backwards and takes human possession of the vast space?

Here, the tree is alone. Have you ever contemplated a tree for itself, for its incrustation in the sky, for its age, for the quality of its wood? Have you ever imagined the extravagant slowness of its life? or felt what it must require of will power, deaf, considered, obstinate, to encircle with bark, and, without nerves and brain, to direct during three hundred years the gushing of its sap?

A mighty tree, painted here all by itself, which envelops and disdains all in its vegetal splendour. But the absent man has left behind the stamp of his reign, and the weight of his power and his body and his death. – Look more carefully: it is a tree loaded down with chains.

That is why the powerful branches are folded back and enfold the trunk: the trunk is pierced and chained by a thick ring – meeting point for the bonds, which spread out from there and go to plunge underground. Ah! you did sense that shame and the bonds, and how, despite the vigour of its limbs, all the leaves sag and weep: this tree was heroic and guilty: it endured that an Emperor – brought to bay in his palace of which the eunuchs left the doors undefended, surrounded by his women agog to see the victor – this tree endured that He hang himself in the top branches and die!

That is all. Do not expect one more dynastic painting. The desire would be sacrilegious towards the Imperial family, the 'Golden Horde', which since two hundred and sixty-six years possesses the present mandate of Heaven, under the seal of the TS'ING..

In that respect, no one would dare to speak of decline or fall, even one in the future ten thousand years hence. Reassuring omens are plentiful every day: the sun observes every day its habit of setting in the West. The seasons follow their order, respectful of the calendar. There are no misplaced heatwaves in winter, nor frosts in the middle of heat. Meteors make their appearances at their given hour, with even more exactitude than ever. Rivers flow logically down to the sea. Alone, the Unicorn – should one admit it? – no longer deigns to be caught. Was he really indispensable to the happiness of villagers, traders, civil and military officers?

On the other hand, evil omens are not more frequent: there are no flagrant monstrosities; not one mulberry tree changed into a willow; not a man turns into a woman. No more inexplicable underground noises are heard. No one has seen bizarre objects appear in the interior of the Palace... nor the invisible Fox take the Emperor's place.

Without doubt, the Underbelly-of-the-Sky is in mourning for several long months yet: That of the Ts'ing, who reigned during the KOUANG-SIU epoch, has gone away, in the Dragon chariot, to drink at the spring of nine fountains ... But the Prince Tch'ouen, his brother, accepting the Regency, has immediately shown the best intentions and the most ordinary qualities. No one in the Palace can claim, in our era SIUAN-T'ONG, to imitate any one of the equivocal or harsh characteristics which in sequence caused the falls of HSIA, CHANG, TCHEOU - HAN, SOUEI, T'ANG - SONG, YUAN and MING . . . Even less would anyone dare to assume a single one of the giant gestures of Che-Houang-Ti, Emperor One.

And it would be a new historical and moral sacrilege to evoke here and now the painting of Long-Yu, living Empress, exemplary widow. How could one imagine her in the guise of Mei-hsi, granting her antique favours to young actors! It is in fact impossible to discern who could be the Grand Usurper among the princes of the blood. That is why the Prince Ts'ing, Great Ancestor of the blood, devotes his experience and prestige of his seventy-eight years solely to looking after his goods and his property. The Great Councillor Na-t'ong is as fearful to do harm as he is of it being done to him, and thus he demonstrates a well-balanced virtue. One is unable any longer to incriminate – as so often during reigns – the intrigues of false eunuchs: from now on all have their diplomas.

And to finish with historical allusions, so praiseworthy in literature, sacrilegious and ill-suited in reference to the Reigning House, we shall agree that no famous philosopher rises up in the wake of those mightily active logicians, whose talent ruined the Song era. No illustrious traveller – no traveller – claims any more, like Yang-ti of Souei, to carry with him the décor and grid plan of his city; but, politely, those who emigrate, immediately take on the habits and customs of the foreigner. Nobody, finally, would have that rash bad taste of Pei-Tcheou: to sanctify himself. It is unacceptable to wish to be accepted as a god. People still drink, but today's wine no longer leads to great cosmological debates: less strong, it is easily vomited. On the other hand, does the question of sanctity or ecstacy ever arise? Pure reason is preferred; in like manner those mad cavalry sorties have long ago been abandoned, which carried so far into the unknown those mighty Western Han – and which, in the *furia* of the race, only led after all into the desert . . . And nowadays people travel in mule carts, in porters' chairs, or in little cars with 'tyres'.

Thus, no literary figure, no Politician, no Poet, no

Statesman – no Man finally – would know how to arise and help or oppose a government and an era as calm and flat as the face of the sea when abandoned by the wind. The Empire squats on its security. A few wicked souls, a few students of European doctrines make ready, they say, a 'revolution'. They only perturb the trade and the moods of the coastal merchants . . .

*

*   *

The succession of dynastic falls stops then and must terminate with the Liberation of Ming. The painter, who tried to illustrate so the declines and the catastrophies, avers he is powerless to produce in their wake the image, above all a truthful one, of the present Thing.

To replace high colours and fine drawing, alone, these words poetically chosen and engraved on the final seal, can depict it:

OFFICIAL GRANDEUR
OF TS'ING

AT PEIKING,
DURING THE . . .

3rd YEAR OF THE
SIUAN-T'ONG PERIOD

That is all. It is over . . . What are you waiting for? You are there: you have listened to me right until the end. Thank you. I am grateful to you, my companions, my accomplices: you have allowed me to steep in unconfined air these Paintings folded too long in my innermost self. They obsessed me with their will to be seen. Now I can look elsewhere.

But you, carry them off in the depths of your eyes. And do not believe that the words I said contain all that Light and Joy sketch in the place that is the world – whether it be in China, or elsewhere, or here around you . . .

So many things, half-seen, can never be seen.

QUARTET ENCOUNTERS

Aharon Appelfeld · *The Retreat*

Alain · *The Gods*

Gabriele D'Annunzio · *The Flame*

Ramón Pérez de Ayala · *Belarmino and Apolonio*

Ramón Pérez de Ayala · *Honeymoon, Bittermoon*

Gaston Bachelard · *The Psychoanalysis of Fire*

Giorgio Bassani · *The Garden of the Finzi-Continis*

Thomas Bernhard · *Concrete*

Robert Bresson · *Notes on the Cinematographer*

Hermann Broch · *The Guiltless*

Hermann Broch · *The Sleepwalkers*

E.M. Cioran · *A Short History of Decay*

E.M. Cioran · *The Temptation to Exist*

René Crevel · *Babylon*

Stig Dagerman · *A Burnt Child*

Stig Dagerman · *The Games of Night*

Stig Dagerman · *German Autumn*

Grazia Deledda · *After the Divorce*

Grazia Deledda · *Cosima*

Heimito von Doderer · *The Demons*

Marcellus Emants · *A Posthumous Confession*

Peter Paul Fuchs (ed.) · *The Music Theatre of Walter Felsenstein*

Carlo Emilio Gadda · *That Awful Mess on Via Merulana*

Andrea Giovene · *Sansevero*

Julien Green · *Avarice House*

Julien Green · *Each Man in His Darkness*

Julien Green · *Moira*

Martin A. Hansen · *The Liar*

Eugene Ionesco · *Fragments of a Journal*

Gustav Janouch · *Conversations with Kafka*

Ismaïl Kadaré · *The General of the Dead Army*

Dezső Kosztolányi · *Anna Édes*

Miroslav Krleža · *On the Edge of Reason*

Miroslav Krleža · *The Return of Philip Latinowicz*

Pär Lagerkvist · *The Dwarf*

Pär Lagerkvist · *Guest of Reality*

Valery Larbaud · *A.O. Barnabooth: His Diary*

Valery Larbaud · *Fermina Marquez*

Arnošt Lustig · *Darkness Casts no Shadow*

Arnošt Lustig · *Diamonds of the Night*

Arnošt Lustig · *Night and Hope*

Osip Mandelstam · *The Noise of Time*

Ana María Matute · *School of the Sun*

Henry de Montherlant · *The Bachelors*

Stratis Myrivilis · *Life in the Tomb*

Romola Nijinsky (ed.) · *The Diary of Vaslav Nijinsky*

Pier Paolo Pasolini · *A Dream of Something*

Fernando Pessoa · *The Book of Disquiet*

Luigi Pirandello · *Short Stories*

D.R. Popescu · *The Royal Hunt*

Vasco Pratolini · *Family Chronicle*

Rainer Maria Rilke · *Rodin and Other Prose Pieces*

Rainer Maria Rilke · *Selected Letters*

Lou Andreas-Salomé · *The Freud Journal*

Victor Segalen · *Paintings*

Victor Segalen · *René Leys*

Fyodor Sologub · *The Petty Demon*

Boris Vian · *Froth on the Daydream*

Boris Vian · *Heartsnatcher*

Elio Vittorini · *Conversation in Sicily*

Bruno Walter · *Gustav Mahler*

Stanislaw Ignacy Witkiewicz · *Insatiability*

Yevgeny Zamyatin · *A Soviet Heretic*